THE PHYSICAL PRINCIPLES OF THE QUANTUM THEORY

By

WERNER HEISENBERG

Professor of Physics, University of Leipzig

Translated into English by

CARL ECKART AND FRANK C. HOYT

Department of Physics, University of Chicago

DOVER PUBLICATIONS, INC.

 PUBLISHED JULY 1930

Library of Congress Catalog Card Number: 49-11952

Manufactured in the United States of America

Dover Publications, Inc.
180 Varick Street
New York 14, New York

FOREWORD TO THE ENGLISH EDITION

It is an unusual pleasure to present Professor Heisenberg's Chicago lectures on "The Physical Principles of the Quantum Theory" to a wider audience than could attend them when they were originally delivered. Professor Heisenberg's leading place in the development of the new quantum mechanics is well recognized by those who have been following its growth. It was in fact he who first saw clearly that in the older forms of quantum theory we were describing our spectra in terms of atomic mechanisms regarding which we could gain no definite knowledge, and who first found a way to interpret (or at least describe) spectroscopic phenomena without assuming the existence of such atomic mechanisms. Likewise, "the uncertainty principle" has become a household phrase throughout our universities, and it is especially fortunate to have this opportunity of learning its significance from one who is responsible for its formulation.

The power of the new quantum mechanics in giving us a better understanding of events on an atomic scale is becoming increasingly evident. The structure of the helium atom, the existence of half-quantum numbers in band spectra, the continuous spatial distribution of photo-electrons, and the phenomenon of radioactive disintegration, to mention only a few examples, are achievements of the new theory which had baffled the old. While the writing of this chapter of the history of physics is doubtless not yet complete, it has progressed to such a stage that we may profitably pause and consider the significance of what has been written. As we make this survey, we are indeed fortunate to have Professor Heisenberg to guide our thoughts.

ARTHUR H. COMPTON

PREFACE

The lectures which I gave at the University of Chicago in the spring of 1929 afforded me the opportunity of reviewing the fundamental principles of quantum theory. Since the conclusive studies of Bohr in 1927 there have been no essential changes in these principles, and many new experiments have confirmed important consequences of the theory (for example, the Raman effect). But even today the physicist more often has a kind of faith in the correctness of the new principles than a clear understanding of them. For this reason the publication of these Chicago lectures in the form of a small book seems justified.

Since the formal mathematical apparatus of the quantum theory is already available in several excellent texts and is more familiar to many than the physical principles, I have placed it at the end of the book, in what is little more than a collection of formulas.[1] In the text itself I have been at pains to use only elementary formulas and calculations, so far as this is possible.

In the body of the text particular emphasis has been

[1] TRANSLATORS' NOTE.—In the English edition, Professor Heisenberg's lectures on the mathematical part of the theory have been reproduced in more detail. This seemed advisable since a treatment of the general transformation theory and the quantum theory of wave fields was not available in English at the time the manuscript was prepared. The former has since been treated in several texts (E. U. Condon and P. M. Morse, *Quantum Mechanics;* A. E. Ruark and H. C. Urey, *Atoms, Molecules and Quanta;* both published by McGraw-Hill).

The English text also deviates in several other points from the German, but these are felt to be unessential changes.

placed on the complete equivalence of the corpuscular and wave concepts, which is clearly reflected in the newer formulations of the mathematical theory. This symmetry of the book with respect to the words "particle" and "wave" shows that nothing is gained by discussing fundamental problems (such as causality) in terms of one rather than the other. I have also attempted to make the distinction between waves in space-time and the Schrödinger waves in configuration space as clear as possible.

On the whole the book contains nothing that is not to be found in previous publications, particularly in the investigations of Bohr. The purpose of the book seems to me to be fulfilled if it contributes somewhat to the diffusion of that "*Kopenhagener Geist der Quantentheorie,*" if I may so express myself, which has directed the entire development of modern atomic physics.

My thanks are due in the first place to Drs. C. Eckart and F. Hoyt, of the University of Chicago, who have taken on themselves not only the labor of preparing the English translation, but have also contributed essentially to the improvement of the book by working over several sections and giving me the benefit of their advice. I am also indebted to Dr. G. Beck for reading proof of the German edition and for valuable assistance in the preparation of the manuscript.

W. HEISENBERG

LEIPZIG
March 3, 1930

CONTENTS

CHAPTER I

INTRODUCTORY

§ 1. THEORY AND EXPERIMENT

The experiments of physics and their results can be described in the language of daily life. Thus if the physicist did not demand a theory to explain his results and could be content, say, with a description of the lines appearing on photographic plates, everything would be simple and there would be no need of an epistemological discussion. Difficulties arise only in the attempt to classify and synthesize the results, to establish the relation of cause and effect between them—in short, to construct a theory. This synthetic process has been applied not only to the results of scientific experiment, but, in the course of ages, also to the simplest experiences of daily life, and in this way all concepts have been formed. In the process, the solid ground of experimental proof has often been forsaken, and generalizations have been accepted uncritically, until finally contradictions between theory and experiment have become apparent. In order to avoid these contradictions, it seems necessary to demand that no concept enter a theory which has not been experimentally verified at least to the same degree of accuracy as the experiments to be explained by the theory. Unfortunately it is quite impossible to fulfil this requirement, since the commonest ideas and words would often be excluded. To avoid these insurmountable difficulties it is found advisable to introduce a great wealth of concepts into a physical theory, without attempting to justify them rigorously, and then to allow experiment to decide at what points a revision is necessary.

Thus it was characteristic of the special theory of relativity that the concepts "measuring rod" and "clock" were subject to searching criticism in the light of experiment; it appeared that these ordinary concepts involved the tacit assumption that there exist (in principle, at least) signals that are propagated with an infinite velocity. When it became evident that such signals were not to be found in nature, the task of eliminating this tacit assumption from all logical deductions was undertaken, with the result that a consistent interpretation was found for facts which had seemed irreconcilable. A much more radical departure from the classical conception of the world was brought about by the general theory of relativity, in which only the concept of coincidence in space-time was accepted uncritically. According to this theory, ordinary language (i.e., classical concepts) is applicable only to the description of experiments in which both the gravitational constant and the reciprocal of the velocity of light may be regarded as negligibly small.

Although the theory of relativity makes the greatest of demands on the ability for abstract thought, still it fulfils the traditional requirements of science in so far as it permits a division of the world into subject and object (observer and observed) and hence a clear formulation of the law of causality. This is the very point at which the difficulties of the quantum theory begin. In atomic physics, the concepts "clock" and "measuring rod" need no immediate consideration, for there is a large field of phenomena in which $1/c$ is negligible. The concepts "space-time coincidence" and "observation," on the other hand, do require a thorough revision. Particularly characteristic of the discussions to follow is the interaction between observer and object; in classical physical theories it has always been assumed either that this interaction is negligibly small, or else that its effect can be eliminated from the result by calculations based on "control" experiments. This assumption is not permissible in atomic physics; the interaction between observer and object causes uncontrollable and large changes in the system being observed, because of the discontinuous changes characteristic of atomic processes. The immediate consequence of this circumstance is that in general every experiment performed to determine some numerical quantity renders the knowledge of others illusory, since the uncontrollable perturbation of the observed system alters the values of previously determined quantities. If this perturbation be followed in its quantitative details, it appears that in many cases it is impossible to obtain an exact determination of the simultaneous values of two variables, but rather that there is a lower limit to the accuracy with which they can be known.[1]

The starting-point of the critique of the relativity theory was the postulate that there is no signal velocity greater than that of light. In a similar manner, this lower limit to the accuracy with which certain variables can be known simultaneously may be postulated as a law of nature (in the form of the so-called uncertainty relations)

[1] W. Heisenberg, *Zeitschrift für Physik*, **43**, 172, 1927.

and made the starting-point of the critique which forms the subject matter of the following pages. These uncertainty relations give us that measure of freedom from the limitations of classical concepts which is necessary for a consistent description of atomic processes. The program of the following considerations will therefore be: first, to obtain a general survey of all concepts whose introduction is suggested by the atomic experiments; second, to limit the range of application of these concepts; and third, to show that the concepts thus limited, together with the mathematical formulation of quantum theory, form a self-consistent scheme.

§2. THE FUNDAMENTAL CONCEPTS OF QUANTUM THEORY

The most important concepts of atomic physics can be induced from the following experiments:

a) *Wilson*[1] *photographs.*—The α- and β-rays emitted by radioactive elements cause the condensation of minute droplets when allowed to pass through supersaturated water vapor. These drops are not distributed at random, but are arranged along definite tracks which, in the case of α-rays (Fig. 1), are nearly straight lines, in the case of β-rays, are irregularly curved. The existence of the tracks and their continuity show that the rays may appropriately be regarded as streams of minute particles moving at high speeds. As is well known, the mass and charge of these particles may be determined from the deflection of the rays by electric and magnetic fields.

[1] *Proceedings of the Royal Society*, A, **85**, 285, 1911; see also *Jahrbuch der Radioaktivität*, **10**, 34, 1913.

b) *Diffraction of matter waves* (*Davisson and Germer*;[1] *Thomson*,[2] *Rupp*[3]).—After the conception of β-rays as streams of particles had remained unchallenged for more than fifteen years, another series of experiments was per-

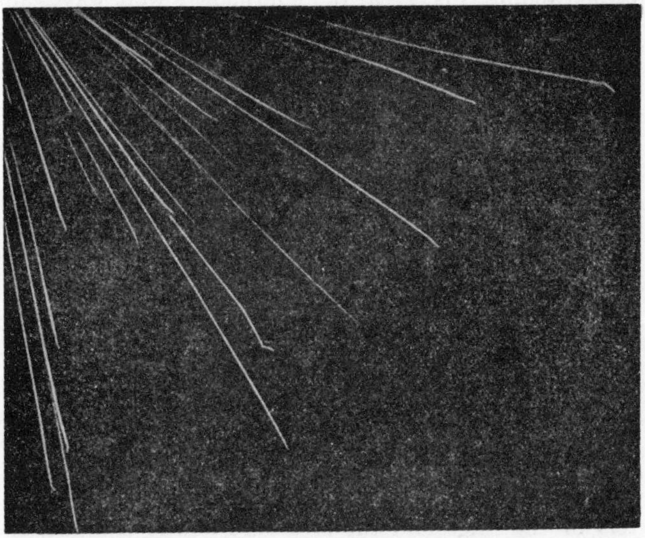

FIG. 1.—Tracks of α-particles in Wilson Chamber

formed which indicated that they could be diffracted and were capable of interference as if they were waves. Typical of these experiments is that of G. P. Thomson, in which a narrow beam of artificial β-rays of moderate

[1] *Physical Review*, **30**, 705, 1927; *Proceedings of the National Academy*, **14**, 317, 1928.

[2] *Proceedings of the Royal Society*, A, **117**, 600, 1928; A, **119**, 651, 1928.

[3] *Annalen der Physik*, **85**, 981, 1928.

energy is passed through a thin foil of matter. The foil is composed of minute crystals oriented at random, but the atoms in each crystal are regularly arranged. A photographic plate receiving the emergent rays exhibits rings of blackening (Fig. 2), as though the rays were waves and were diffracted by the minute crystals. From the diame-

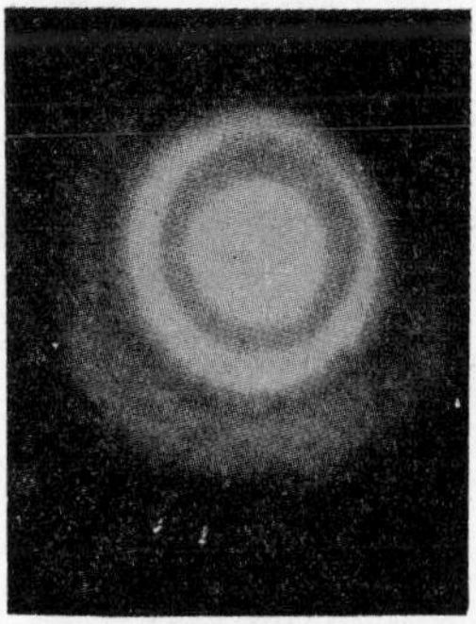

FIG. 2.—Diffraction of electrons on passing through a thin foil of matter.

ters of the rings and the structure of the crystals, the length of these waves may be determined and is found to be $\lambda = h/mv$, where m is the mass and v the velocity of the particles as determined by the above-mentioned experiments. Similar experiments were performed by Davisson and Germer, Kikuchi,[1] and Rupp.

c) The diffraction of X-rays.—The same dual interpretation is necessary in the case of light and electromagnetic radiation in general. After Newton's objections to

[1] *Japanese Journal of Physics*, 5, 83, 1928.

the wave theory of light had been refuted and the phenomena of interference explained by Fresnel, this theory dominated all others for many years, until Einstein[1] pointed out that the experiments of Lenard on the photoelectric effect could only be explained by a corpuscular theory. He postulated that the momentum of the hypothetical particles was related to the wave-length of the radiation by the formula $p=h/\lambda$ (cf. § 2*b*). The necessity for both interpretations is particularly clear in the case of X-rays: If a homogeneous beam of X-rays is passed through a crystalline mass, and the emergent rays received on a photographic plate (Fig. 3), the result is much like the result of G. P. Thomson's experiment, and it may be concluded that X-rays are a form of wave motion, with a determinable wave-length.

d) *The Compton-Simon*[2] *experiment*.—When a beam of X-rays passes through supersaturated water vapor, it is scattered by the molecules. Secondary products of the scattering are the "recoil" electrons, which are apparently particles of considerable energy, since they form tracks of condensed droplets as do the β-rays. These tracks are not very long, however, and occur with random direction. They apparently originate within the region traversed by the primary X-ray beam. Other secondary products of the scattering are the photoelectrons, which again make themselves evident by longer tracks of condensed water droplets. Under suitable conditions these tracks originate at points outside the primary X-ray beam, but the two secondary products are not unrelated.

[1] *Annalen der Physik*, **17**, 145, 1905. [2] *Physical Review*, **25**, 306, 1925.

If it be assumed that the X-ray beam consists of a stream of light-particles (photons) and that the scattering process is the collision of a photon with one of the electrons of the molecule, as a result of which the electron recoils in the observed direction, Einstein's postulate regarding the

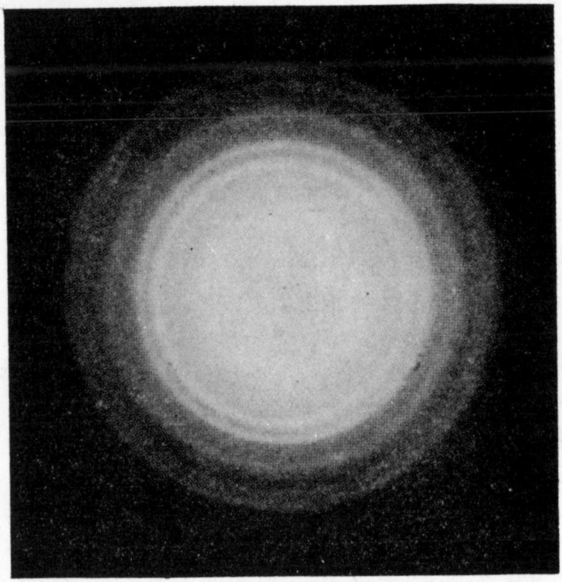

FIG. 3.—Diffraction of X-rays by MgO powder

energy and momentum of the photons enables the direction of the photon after the collision to be calculated. This photon then collides with a second molecule, and gives up its remaining energy to an electron (the photo-electron). This assumption has been quantitatively verified (Fig. 4).

e) *The collision experiments of Franck and Hertz.*[1]—When a beam of slow electrons with homogeneous velocity passes through a gas, the electronic current as function of the velocity changes discontinuously at certain values of the velocity (energy). The analysis of these experiments leads to the conclusion that the atoms in the

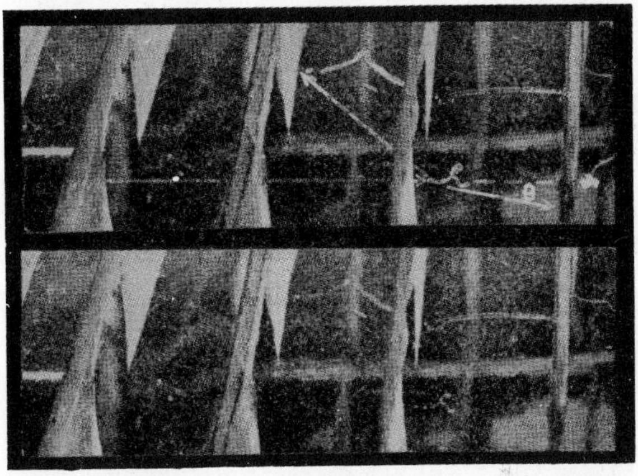

FIG. 4.—Photograph showing recoil electron and associated photo electron liberated by X-rays. The upper photograph is retouched.

gas can only assume discrete energy values (Bohr's postulate). When the energy of the atom is known, one speaks of a "stationary state of the atom." When the kinetic energy of the electron is too small to change the atom from its stationary state to a higher one, the electron makes only elastic collisions with the atoms, but when the kinetic energy suffices for excitation some electrons will transfer their energy to the atom, so the elec-

[1] *Verhandlungen der Deutschen Physikalische Gesellschaft*, **15**, 613, 1913.

tronic current as a function of the velocity changes rapidly in the critical region. The concept of stationary states, which is suggested by these experiments, is the most direct expression of the discontinuity in all atomic processes.

From these experiments it is seen that both matter and radiation possess a remarkable duality of character, as they sometimes exhibit the properties of waves, at other times those of particles. Now it is obvious that a thing cannot be a form of wave motion and composed of particles at the same time—the two concepts are too different. It is true that it might be postulated that two separate entities, one having all the properties of a particle, and the other all the properties of wave motion, were combined in some way to form "light." But such theories are unable to bring about the intimate relation between the two entities which seems required by the experimental evidence. As a matter of fact, it is experimentally certain only that light sometimes behaves as if it possessed some of the attributes of a particle, but there is no experiment which proves that it possesses all the properties of a particle; similar statements hold for matter and wave motion. The solution of the difficulty is that the two mental pictures which experiments lead us to form—the one of particles, the other of waves—are both incomplete and have only the validity of analogies which are accurate only in limiting cases. It is a trite saying that "analogies cannot be pushed too far," yet they may be justifiably used to describe things for which our language has no words. Light and matter are both single entities, and the apparent duality arises in the limitations of our language.

It is not surprising that our language should be incapable of describing the processes occurring within the atoms, for, as has been remarked, it was invented to describe the experiences of daily life, and these consist only of processes involving exceedingly large numbers of atoms. Furthermore, it is very difficult to modify our language so that it will be able to describe these atomic processes, for words can only describe things of which we can form mental pictures, and this ability, too, is a result of daily experience. Fortunately, mathematics is not subject to this limitation, and it has been possible to invent a mathematical scheme—the quantum theory—which seems entirely adequate for the treatment of atomic processes; for visualization, however, we must content ourselves with two incomplete analogies—the wave picture and the corpuscular picture. The simultaneous applicability of both pictures is thus a natural criterion to determine how far each analogy may be "pushed" and forms an obvious starting-point for the critique of the concepts which have entered atomic theories in the course of their development, for, obviously, uncritical deduction of consequences from both will lead to contradictions. In this way one obtains the limitations of the concept of a particle by considering the concept of a wave. As N. Bohr[1] has shown, this is the basis of a very simple derivation of the uncertainty relations between co-ordinate and momentum of a particle. In the same manner one may derive the limitations of the concept of a wave by comparison with the concept of a particle.

It must be emphasized that this critique cannot be car-

[1] *Nature*, **121**, 580, 1928; *Naturwissenschaften*, **16**, 245, 1928.

ried through entirely without using the mathematical apparatus of the quantum theory, for the development of the latter preceded the clarification of the physical principles in the historic sequence. In order to avoid obscuring the essential relationships by too much mathematics, however, it has seemed advisable to relegate this formalism to the Appendix. The exposition of mathematical principles given there does not pretend to be complete, but only to furnish the reader with those formulas which are essential for the argument of the text. References to this Appendix are given as A (16), etc.

CHAPTER II

CRITIQUE OF THE PHYSICAL CONCEPTS OF THE CORPUSCULAR THEORY OF MATTER

§ 1. THE UNCERTAINTY RELATIONS

The concepts of velocity, energy, etc., have been developed from simple experiments with common objects, in which the mechanical behavior of macroscopic bodies can be described by the use of such words. These same concepts have then been carried over to the electron, since in certain fundamental experiments electrons show a mechanical behavior like that of the objects of common experience. Since it is known, however, that this similarity exists only in a certain limited region of phenomena, the applicability of the corpuscular theory must be limited in a corresponding way. According to Bohr,[1] this restriction may be deduced from the principle that the processes of atomic physics can be visualized equally well in terms of waves or particles. Thus the statement that the position[2] of an electron is known to within a certain accuracy Δx at the time t can be visualized by the picture of a wave packet in the proper position with an approximate extension Δx. By "wave packet" is meant a wavelike disturbance whose amplitude is appreciably different from

[1] N. Bohr, *Nature*, **121**, 580, 1928.

[2] The following considerations apply equally to any of the three space co-ordinates of the electron, therefore only one is treated explicitly.

zero only in a bounded region. This region is, in general, in motion, and also changes its size and shape, i.e., the disturbance spreads. The velocity of the electron corresponds to that of the wave packet, but this latter cannot be exactly defined, because of the diffusion which takes place. This indeterminateness is to be considered as an essential characteristic of the electron, and not as evidence of the inapplicability of the wave picture. Defining momentum as $p_x = \mu v_x$ (where μ = mass of electron, v_x = x-component of velocity), this uncertainty in the velocity causes an uncertainty in p_x of amount Δp_x; from the simplest laws of optics, together with the empirically established law $\lambda = h/p$, it can readily be shown that

$$\Delta x \Delta p_x \geq h . \qquad (1)$$

Suppose the wave packet made up by superposition of plane sinusoidal waves, all with wave-lengths near λ_0. Then, roughly speaking, $n = \Delta x/\lambda_0$ crests or troughs fall within the boundary of the packet. Outside the boundary the component plane waves must cancel by interference; this is possible if, and only if, the set of component waves contains some for which at least $n+1$ waves fall in the critical range. This gives

$$\frac{\Delta x}{\lambda_0 - \Delta\lambda} \geq n+1 ,$$

where $\Delta\lambda$ is the approximate range of wave-lengths necessary to represent the packet. Consequently

$$\frac{\Delta x \Delta\lambda}{\lambda_0^2} \geq 1 . \qquad (2)$$

On the other hand, the group velocity of the waves (i.e., the velocity of the packet) is by A (85)

$$v_g = \frac{h}{\mu\lambda_0} , \qquad (3)$$

so that the spreading of the packet is characterized by the range of velocities

$$\Delta v_g = \frac{h}{\mu\lambda_0^2} \Delta\lambda .$$

By definition $\Delta p_x = \mu \Delta v_g$ and therefore by equation (2),

$$\Delta x \Delta p_x \geq h .$$

This uncertainty relation specifies the limits within which the particle picture can be applied. Any use of the words "position" and "velocity" with an accuracy exceeding that given by equation (1) is just as meaningless as the use of words whose sense is not defined.[1]

The uncertainty relations can also be deduced without explicit use of the wave picture, for they are readily obtained from the mathematical scheme of quantum theory

[1] In this connection one should particularly remember that the human language permits the construction of sentences which do not involve any consequences and which therefore have no content at all—in spite of the fact that these sentences produce some kind of picture in our imagination; e.g., the statement that besides our world there exists another world, with which any connection is impossible in principle, does not lead to any experimental consequence, but does produce a kind of picture in the mind. Obviously such a statement can neither be proved nor disproved. One should be especially careful in using the words "reality," "actually," etc., since these words very often lead to statements of the type just mentioned.

and its physical interpretation.[1] Any knowledge of the co-ordinate q of the electron can be expressed by a probability amplitude $S(q')$, $|S(q')|^2dq'$ being the probability of finding the numerical value of the co-ordinate of the electron between q' and $q'+dq'$. Let

$$\bar{q}=\int q'|S(q')|^2dq' \tag{4}$$

be the average value of q. Then Δq defined by

$$(\Delta q)^2=2\int(q'-\bar{q})^2|S(q')|^2dq' \tag{5}$$

can be called the uncertainty in the knowledge of the electron's position. In an exactly analogous way $|T(p')|^2dp'$ gives the probability of finding the momentum of the electron between p' and $p'+dp'$; again $\bar{p}$ and Δp may be defined as

$$\bar{p}=\int p'|T(p')|^2dp' , \tag{6}$$

$$(\Delta p)^2=2\int(p'-\bar{p})^2|T(p')|^2dp' . \tag{7}$$

By equation A(169), the probability amplitudes are related by the equations

$$\left.\begin{aligned} T(p')&=\int S(q')R(q'p')dq' , \\ S(q')&=\int T(p')R^*(q'p')dp' , \end{aligned}\right\} \tag{8}$$

where $R(q'p')$ is the matrix of the transformation from a Hilbert space in which q is a diagonal matrix to one in which p is diagonal. From equation A(41) we have

$$\int p(q'q'')R(q''p')dq''=\int R(q'p'')p(p''p')dp'' ,$$

[1] Kennard, *Zeitschrift für Physik*, **44**, 326, 1927.

and by equation A(42) this is equivalent to

$$\frac{h}{2\pi i}\frac{\partial}{\partial q'}R(q'p')=p'R(q'p') , \tag{9}$$

whose solution is

$$R=ce^{\frac{2\pi i}{h}p'q'} . \tag{10}$$

Normalizing gives c the value $1/\sqrt{h}$. The values of Δp, Δq are thus not independent. To simplify further calculations, we introduce the following abbreviations:

$$\left.\begin{aligned} x&=q'-\bar{q} , \qquad y=p'-\bar{p} , \\ s(x)&=S(q')e^{\frac{2\pi i}{h}\bar{p}q'} , \\ t(y)&=T(p')e^{-\frac{2\pi i}{h}\bar{q}(p'-\bar{p})} . \end{aligned}\right\} \tag{11}$$

Then equations (5) and (7) become

$$(\Delta q)^2=2\int x^2|s(x)|^2dx , \tag{5a}$$

$$(\Delta p)^2=2\int y^2|t(y)|^2dy , \tag{7a}$$

while equations (8) become

$$\begin{aligned} t(y)&=\frac{1}{\sqrt{h}}\int s(x)e^{\frac{2\pi i}{h}xy}dx , \\ s(x)&=\frac{1}{\sqrt{h}}\int t(y)e^{-\frac{2\pi i}{h}xy}dy . \end{aligned} \tag{8a}$$

Combining (5*a*), (7*a*), and (8*a*), the expression for $(\Delta p)^2$ may be transformed, giving

$$\tfrac{1}{2}(\Delta p)^2 = \frac{1}{\sqrt{h}}\int y^2 t^*(y)dy \int s(x)e^{\frac{2\pi i}{h}xy}dx\,,$$

$$= \frac{1}{\sqrt{h}}\int t^*(y)dy \int s(x)\left(\frac{h}{2\pi i}\frac{d}{dx}\right)^2 e^{\frac{2\pi i}{h}xy}dx\,,$$

$$= \frac{1}{\sqrt{h}}\left(\frac{h}{2\pi i}\right)^2\int t^*(y)dy \int \frac{d^2s}{dx^2}e^{\frac{2\pi i}{h}xy}dx\,,$$

$$= \left(\frac{h}{2\pi i}\right)^2\int s^*(x)\frac{d^2s}{dx^2}dx\,,$$

or

$$\tfrac{1}{2}(\Delta p)^2 = \frac{h^2}{4\pi^2}\int\left|\frac{ds}{dx}\right|^2 dx\,. \tag{12}$$

Now

$$\left|\frac{ds}{dx}\right|^2 \geq \frac{1}{(\Delta q)^2}|s(x)|^2 - \frac{d}{dx}\left(\frac{x}{(\Delta q)^2}|s(x)|^2\right) - \frac{x^2}{(\Delta q)^4}|s(x)|^2\,, \tag{13}$$

as may be proved by rearranging the obvious relation

$$\left|\frac{x}{(\Delta q)^2}s(x) + \frac{ds}{dx}\right|^2 \geq 0\,. \tag{13a}$$

Hence it follows from equation (12) that

$$\left.\begin{aligned} &\tfrac{1}{2}(\Delta p)^2 \geq \tfrac{1}{2}\frac{h^2}{4\pi^2}\frac{1}{(\Delta q)^2}\,,\\ \text{or}\quad &\\ &\Delta p\Delta q \geq \frac{h}{2\pi}\,, \end{aligned}\right\} \tag{14}$$

which was to be proved. The equality can be true in (14) only when the left side of (13a) vanishes, i.e., when

$$\left.\begin{aligned} s(x) &= ce^{-\frac{x^2}{2(\Delta q)^2}}, \\ \text{or} \qquad S(q') &= ce^{-\frac{(q'-\bar{q})^2}{2(\Delta q)^2} - \frac{2\pi i}{h}\bar{p}q'}, \end{aligned}\right\} \qquad (15)$$

where c is an arbitrary constant. Thus the Gaussian probability distribution causes the product $\Delta p \Delta q$ to assume its minimum value.

It must be emphasized again that this proof does not differ at all in mathematical content from that given at the beginning of this section on the basis of the duality between the wave and corpuscular pictures of atomic phenomena. The first proof, if carried through precisely, would also involve all the equations (4)–(14). Physically, the last proof appears to be more general than the former, which was proved on the assumption that x was a cartesian co-ordinate and applies specifically only to free electrons because of the relation $\lambda = h/\mu v_g$ which enters into the proof. Equation (14), on the other hand, applies to any pair of canonic conjugates p and q. This greater generality of (14) is rather specious, however. As Bohr[1] has emphasized, if a measurement of its co-ordinate is to be possible at all, the electron must be practically free.

[1] *Loc. cit.*

§ 2. ILLUSTRATIONS OF THE UNCERTAINTY RELATIONS

The uncertainty principle refers to the degree of indeterminateness in the possible present knowledge of the simultaneous values of various quantities with which the quantum theory deals; it does not restrict, for example, the exactness of a position measurement alone or a velocity measurement alone. Thus suppose that the velocity of a free electron is precisely known, while the position is completely unknown. Then the principle states that every subsequent observation of the position will alter the momentum by an unknown and undeterminable amount such that after carrying out the experiment our knowledge of the electronic motion is restricted by the uncertainty relation. This may be expressed in concise and general terms by saying that every experiment destroys some of the knowledge of the system which was obtained by previous experiments. This formulation makes it clear that the uncertainty relation does not refer to the past; if the velocity of the electron is at first known and the position then exactly measured, the position for times previous to the measurement may be calculated. Then for these past times $\Delta p \Delta q$ is smaller than the usual limiting value, but this knowledge of the past is of a purely speculative character, since it can never (because of the unknown change in momentum caused by the position measurement) be used as an initial condition in any calculation of the future progress of the electron and thus cannot be subjected to experimental verification. It is a matter of personal belief whether such a calculation concerning the past history of the electron can be ascribed any physical reality or not.

a) Determination of the position of a free particle.—As a first example of the destruction of the knowledge of a particle's momentum by an apparatus determining its position, we consider the use of a microscope.[1] Let the particle be moving at such a distance from the microscope that the cone of rays scattered from it through the objective has an angular opening ϵ. If λ is the wave-length of the light illuminating it, then the uncertainty in the measurement of the x-co-ordinate (see Fig. 5) according to the laws of optics governing the resolving power of any instrument is:

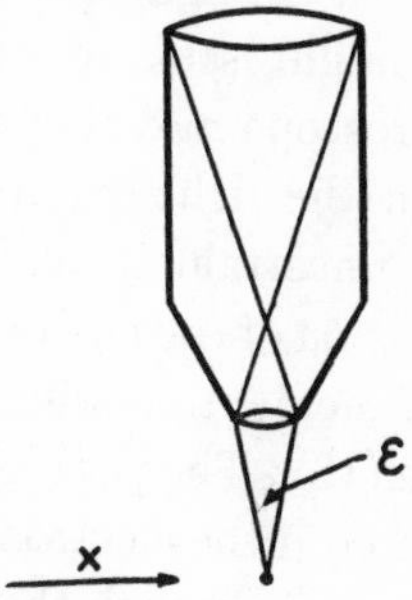

FIG. 5

$$\Delta x = \frac{\lambda}{\sin \epsilon} . \tag{16}$$

But, for any measurement to be possible at least one photon must be scattered from the electron and pass through the microscope to the eye of the observer. From this photon the electron receives a Compton recoil of order of magnitude h/λ. The recoil cannot be exactly known, since the direction of the scattered photon is undetermined within the bundle of rays entering the microscope. Thus there is an uncertainty of the recoil in the x-direction of amount

$$\Delta p_x \sim \frac{h}{\lambda} \sin \epsilon , \tag{17}$$

and it follows that for the motion after the experiment

$$\Delta p_x \Delta x \sim h . \tag{18}$$

[1] N. Bohr, *loc. cit.*

Objections may be raised to this consideration; the indeterminateness of the recoil is due to the uncertain path of the light quantum within the bundle of rays, and we might seek to determine the path by making the microscope movable and measuring the recoil it receives from the light quantum. But this does not circumvent the uncertainty relation, for it immediately raises the question of the position of the microscope, and its position and momentum will also be found to be subject to equation (18). The position of the microscope need not be considered if the electron and a fixed scale be simultaneously observed through the moving microscope, and this seems to afford an escape from the uncertainty principle. But an observation then requires the simultaneous passage of at least two light quanta through the microscope to the observer—one from the electron and one from the scale—and a measurement of the recoil of the microscope is no longer sufficient to determine the direction of the light scattered by the electron. And so on *ad infinitum*.

One might also try to improve the accuracy by measuring the maximum of the diffraction pattern produced by the microscope. This is only possible when many photons co-operate, and a calculation shows that the error in measurement of x is reduced to $\Delta x = \lambda/\sqrt{m} \sin \epsilon$ when m photons produce the pattern. On the other hand, each photon contributes to the unknown change in the electron's momentum, the result being $\Delta p_x = \sqrt{m}\, h \sin \epsilon/\lambda$ (addition of independent errors). The relation (18) is thus not avoided.

It is characteristic of the foregoing discussion that simultaneous use is made of deductions from the corpuscular and wave theories of light, for, on the one hand, we speak of resolving power, and, on the other hand, of photons and the recoils resulting from their collision with the particle under consideration. This is avoided, in so far as the theory of light is concerned, in the following considerations.

If electrons are made to pass through a slit of width d (Fig. 6), then their co-ordinates in the direction of this width are known at the moment after having passed it with the accuracy $\Delta x = d$. If we assume the momentum in this direction to have been zero before passing through the slit (normal incidence), it would appear that the uncertainty relation is not fulfilled. But the electron may also be considered to be a plane de Broglie wave, and it is at once apparent that diffraction phenomena are necessarily produced by the slit. The emergent beam has a finite angle of divergence α, which is, by the simplest laws of optics,

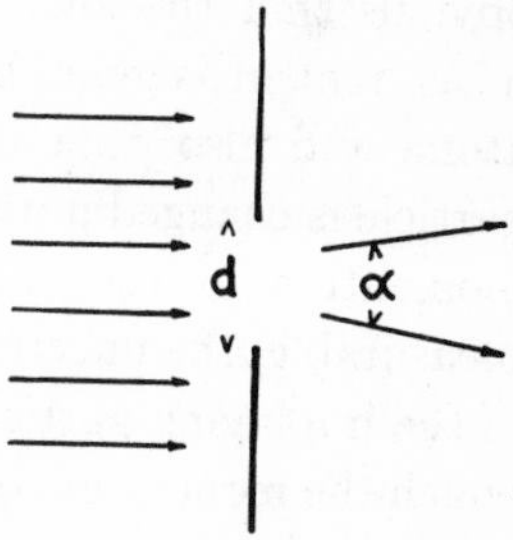

FIG. 6

$$\sin \alpha \sim \frac{\lambda}{d}, \tag{19}$$

where λ is the wave-length of the de Broglie waves. Thus the momentum of the electron parallel to the screen is uncertain, after passing through the slit, by an amount

$$\Delta p = \frac{h}{\lambda} \sin \alpha \tag{20}$$

since h/λ is the momentum of the electron in the direction of the beam. Then, since $\Delta x = d$,

$$\Delta x \Delta p \sim h .$$

In this discussion we have avoided the dual character of light, but have made extensive use of the two theories of the electron.

As a last method of determining position we discuss the well-known method of observing scintillations produced by α-rays when they are received on a fluorescent screen or of observing their tracks in a Wilson chamber. The essential point of these methods is that the position of the particle is indicated by the ionization of an atom; it is obvious that the lower limit to the accuracy of such a measurement is given by the linear dimension Δq_s of the atom, and also that the momentum of the impinging particle is changed during the act of ionization. Since the momentum of the electron ejected from the atom is measurable, the uncertainty in the change of momentum of the impinging particle is equal to the range Δp_s within which the momentum of this electron varies while moving in its un-ionized orbit. This variation in momentum is again related to the size of the atom by the inequality

$$\Delta p_s \Delta q_s \geq h \ .$$

Later discussion will show, in fact, that quite generally[1]

$$\Delta p_s \Delta q_s \sim nh \ ,$$

where n is the quantum number of the stationary state concerned (cf. § 2c below). Thus the uncertainty relation also governs this type of position measurement; here the dualism of treatment is relegated to the background, and

[1] N. Bohr, *loc. cit.*

the uncertainty relation appears rather to be the result of the Bohr quantum conditions determining the stationary state, but naturally the quantum conditions are themselves manifestations of the duality.

b) Measurement of the velocity or momentum of a free particle.—The simplest and most fundamental method of measuring velocity depends on the determination of position at two different times. If the time interval elapsing between the position measurements is sufficiently large, it is possible to determine the velocity before the second was made with any desired accuracy, but it is the velocity after this measurement which alone is of importance to the physicist, and this cannot be determined with exactness. The change in momentum which is necessarily produced by the last observation is subject to such an indeterminateness that the uncertainty relation is again fulfilled, as has been shown in the last section.

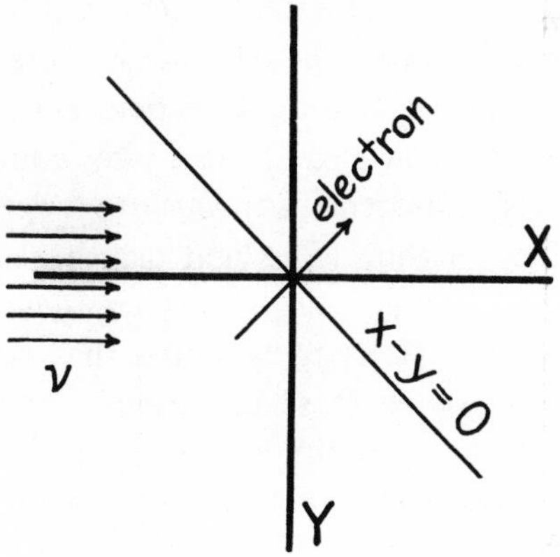

FIG. 7

Another common method of determining the velocity of charged particles makes use of the Doppler effect. Figure 7 shows the experimental arrangement in its essentials. The component, p_x, of the electron's momentum may be supposed to be known with ideal exactness, its x-co-ordinate therefore completely unknown. On the other hand, the y-co-ordinate of the electron will be assumed to have been accurately determined, and p_y correspondingly unknown. The problem is therefore to determine the velocity in the y-direction, and it is to be shown that the knowledge of the y-co-ordinate is destroyed by this measurement to the extent demanded by the uncertainty relation. The light may be supposed incident along the x-axis, and the scattered light observed in the y-direction. (It is to be noted that the Doppler effect vanishes, under these conditions, if the electron moves along the straight line $x-y=0$.) The theory of the Doppler effect is in this case identical with that of the Compton effect, and it is only necessary to use the laws of conservation of energy and momentum of the electron and light quantum. Letting E denote the energy of the electron, ν the frequency of the incident light, and using primes to distinguish the same quantity before and after the collision, we have

$$\left.\begin{aligned} h\nu+E&=h\nu'+E' ,\\ \frac{h\nu}{c}+p_x&=p_x' ,\\ p_y&=\frac{h\nu'}{c}+p_y' ,\end{aligned}\right\} \qquad (21)$$

whence

$$\left.\begin{aligned} h(\nu-\nu') &= E'-E\,, \\ &= \frac{1}{2\mu}[p_x'^2+p_y'^2-p_x^2-p_y^2]\,, \\ &\sim \frac{1}{\mu}[(p_x'-p_x)p_x+(p_y'-p_y)p_y]\,, \\ &= \frac{1}{\mu}\left[\frac{h\nu}{c}\,p_x-\frac{h\nu'}{c}\,p_y\right], \\ &\sim \frac{h\nu}{\mu c}\,(p_x-p_y)\,. \end{aligned}\right\} \qquad (22)$$

Since it is assumed that p_x and ν are known, the accuracy of the determination of p_y is conditioned only by the accuracy with which the frequency ν' of the scattered light is measured:

$$\Delta p_y' = \frac{\mu c}{\nu}\,\Delta\nu'\,. \qquad (23)$$

To determine ν' with this accuracy, it is necessary to observe a train of waves of finite length, which in turn demands a finite time:

$$T = \frac{1}{\Delta\nu'}\,.$$

As it is unknown whether the photon collided with the electron at the beginning or at the end of this time interval, it is also unknown whether the electron moved with the velocity $(1/\mu)p_y$ or $(1/\mu)p_y'$ during this time. The uncertainty in the position of the electron which is produced by this cause is thus

$$\Delta y = \frac{1}{\mu}\,(p_y-p_y')T = \frac{h\nu}{c\mu}\,T\,,$$

whence

$$\Delta p_y \Delta y \sim h \, .$$

A third method of velocity measurement depends on the deflection of charged particles by a magnetic field. For this purpose a beam must be defined by a slit, whose width will be designated by *d*. This ray then enters a homogeneous magnetic field, whose direction is to be taken perpendicular to the plane of Figure 8. The length of that part of the ray which lies in the region of the field may be *a;* after leaving this region, the ray traverses a field-free region of length *l* and then passes through a second slit also of width *d*, whose position determines the angle of deflection α. The velocity of the particles in the direction of the beam is to be determined from the equation

$$\alpha = \frac{\frac{a}{v} He \frac{v}{c}}{\mu v} = \frac{aHe}{\mu v c} \, . \tag{24}$$

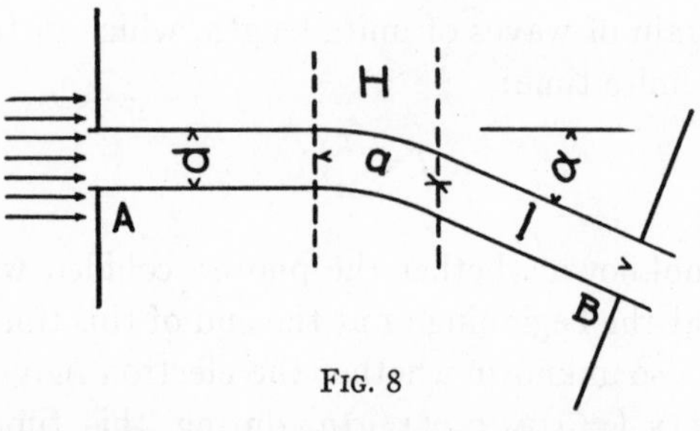

FIG. 8

The corresponding errors in measurement are related by

$$\Delta \alpha = \frac{aHe}{\mu c} \frac{\Delta v}{v^2} \, .$$

It may be supposed that the position of the particle in the direction of the ray was initially known with great accuracy. This may be achieved, for example, by opening the first slit only during a very brief interval. It will again be shown that this knowledge is lost during the experiment in such a manner that the relation $\Delta p \Delta q \sim h$ is fulfilled after the experiment. To begin with, the accuracy with which the angle α can be determined is obviously $d/(l+a)$, but even this accuracy can only be attained if the natural de Broglie scattering of the ray is less than this. Therefore

$$\Delta\alpha \geq \frac{d}{l+a}, \qquad \Delta\alpha \geq \frac{\lambda}{d},$$

whence

$$(\Delta\alpha)^2 \geq \frac{\lambda}{l+a}.$$

The uncertainty in the position of the particle in the ray after the experiment is equal to the product of the time required to pass through the field and reach the second slit and the uncertainty in the velocity. Thus

$$\Delta q \sim \frac{l+a}{v} \Delta v,$$

whence

$$\Delta q \Delta v \sim \frac{l+a}{v} (\Delta v)^2,$$

$$\sim \frac{l+a}{v} \left(\frac{\mu c v}{aHe}\right)^2 (\Delta\alpha)^2,$$

$$\geq \frac{\lambda}{v} \left(\frac{\mu c v^2}{aHe}\right)^2.$$

The terms in the parentheses are equal to v/α and $\lambda = h/\mu v$, whence

$$\mu \Delta q \Delta v \geq \frac{h}{\alpha^2} \geq h,$$

since equation (24) is valid only for small values of α. For large angles of deflection, this derivation requires radical modification. One must remember, among other things, that the experiment as described here would not distinguish between $\alpha=0$ and $\alpha=2\pi$.

c) *Bound electrons.*—If it be required to deduce the uncertainty relations for the position, q, and momentum, p, of bound electrons, two problems must be clearly distinguished. The first assumes that the energy of the system, i.e., its stationary state, is known, and then inquires what accuracy of knowledge of p and q is implied in, or is compatible with, this knowledge of the energy. The second, distinct problem disregards the possibility of determining the energy of the system and merely inquires what the greatest accuracy is with which p and q may simultaneously be known. In this second case, the experiments necessary for the measurement of p and q may produce transitions from one stationary state to another; in the first case, the methods of measurement must be so chosen that transitions are not induced.

We consider the first problem in some detail, and assume an atom in a given stationary state. As Bohr has shown,[1] the corpuscular theory then forces one to conclude that $\Delta p \Delta q$ is in general greater than h. For it is obvious that we are concerned with the variation of p and q as the electron moves in its orbit, and it follows from

$$\int p dq = nh \tag{25}$$

that

$$\Delta q_s \Delta p_s \sim nh \; . \tag{26}$$

This may most readily be comprehended from a diagram of the orbit in phase space as given by classical mechanics

[1] *Ibid.*

(Fig. 9). The integral is nothing else than the area inclosed by the orbit, and $\Delta p_s \Delta q_s$ is obviously of the same order of magnitude. The index *s* which accompanies these uncertainties is to indicate that they are not the absolute minima of these quantities, but are the special values which are assumed by them when the stationary state of the atom is known simultaneously and exactly. This uncertainty is of practical importance, for example, in the discussion of the scintillation method of counting α-particles (chap. ii, § 2*a*). In the classical theory, it would seem strange to consider this as an essential uncertainty, for further experiments could be made without disturbing the orbit. The quantum theory, however, shows that a knowledge of the energy is a "determinate case" (*reiner Fall*),[1] i.e., a case which is represented in the mathematical scheme by a definite wave packet (in configuration space) which does not involve any undetermined constants. This wave packet is the Schrödinger function of the stationary state. If the calculation of pages 16–19 is carried through for this packet, the value of $\Delta p_s \Delta q_s$ is found to be greater in proportion to the number of nodes possessed by the characteristic function. If we consider a function *s* in equation (12) which possesses *n* nodes, the calculation would show that

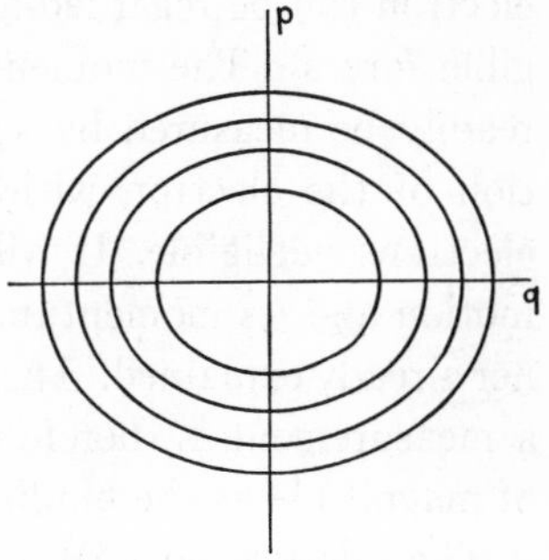

FIG. 9

$$\Delta p_s \Delta q_s \sim nh \ .$$

[1] The translators believe that the literal rendering of the German phrase ("pure case") does not at all convey the concept involved.

To pass on to the second problem: The maximum accuracy is obviously given by $\Delta p \Delta q \sim h$ if all knowledge of the stationary states be disregarded. Then the measurements can be carried out by such violent agents that the electron can be regarded as free (acted on only by negligible forces). The momentum of the electron can most readily be measured by suddenly rendering the interaction of the electron with the nucleus and neighboring electrons negligible. It will then execute a straight-line motion and its momentum can be measured in the manner already explained. The disturbance necessary for such a measurement is therefore obviously of the same order of magnitude as the binding energy of the electron.

The relation [eq. (6)] is of importance, as Bohr points out, for the equivalence of classical and quantum mechanics in the limit of large quantum numbers. This is seen when the validity of the concept of an "orbit" is examined. As the highest accuracy attainable is $\Delta p \Delta q \sim h$, the orbit must be the path of a probability packet whose cross-section ($|S(p')|^2 |S(q')|^2$) is approximately h. Such a packet can describe a well-defined, approximately closed path only if the area inclosed by this path is much greater than the cross-section of the wave packet. This, according to equation (26), is possible only in the limit of large quantum numbers; for small n, on the other hand, the concept of an orbit loses all significance, in phase space as well as in configuration space. It is thus seen to be essential for this limiting equivalence of the two theories that the factor n occurs on the right side of equation (26).

The inapplicability of the concept of an orbit in the region of small quantum numbers can be made clear from direct physical considerations in the following manner: The orbit is the temporal sequence of the points in space at which the electron is observed. As the dimensions of the atom in its lowest state are of the order 10^{-8} cm, it will be necessary to use light of wave-length not greater than 10^{-9} cm in order to carry out a position measurement of sufficient accuracy for the purpose. A single photon of such light is, however, sufficient to remove the electron from the atom, because of the Compton recoil. Only a single point of the hypothetical orbit is thus observable. One can, however, repeat this single observation on a large number of atoms, and thus obtain a probability distribution of the electron in the atom. According to Born, this is given mathematically by $\psi\psi^*$ (or, in the case of several electrons, by the average of this expression taken over the co-ordinates of the other electrons in the atom). This is the physical significance of the statement that $\psi\psi^*$ is the probability of observing the electron at a given point. This result is stranger than it seems at first glance. As is well known, ψ diminishes exponentially with increasing distance from the nucleus; there is thus always a small but finite probability of finding the electron at a great distance from the center of the atom. The potential energy of the electrons is negative at such a point, but very small. The kinetic energy is always positive; so that the total energy is therefore certainly greater than the energy of the stationary state under consideration. This paradox finds its resolution when the energy imparted to the electron by the photon used in making the position measurement is taken into account. This energy is considerably greater than the ionization energy of the electron, and thus suffices to prevent any violation of the law of conservation of energy, as is readily calculated explicitly from the theory of the Compton effect.

This paradox also serves as a warning against carrying out the "statistical interpretation" of quantum mechanics too schematically. Because of the exponential behavior of the Schrödinger function at infinity, the electron will sometimes be found as much as, say, 1 cm from the nucleus. One might suppose that it would be possible to verify the presence of the electron at such a point by the use of red light. This red light would not produce any appreciable Compton recoil and the foregoing paradox would arise once more. As a matter of fact, the red light will not permit such a measurement to be made; the atom as a whole will react with the light according to the formulas of dispersion theory, and the result will not yield any information regarding the position of a given electron in the atom. This may be made plausible if one remembers that (according to the corpuscular theory) the electron will execute a number of rotations about the nucleus during one period of the red light. The statistical predictions of quantum theory are thus significant only when combined with experiments which are actually capable of observing the phenomena treated by the statistics. In many cases it seems better not to speak of the probable position of the electron, but to say that its size depends upon the experiment being performed.

The orbital concept has a significance when applied to highly excited states of the atom; therefore it must be possible to carry out the determination of the position of the electron with an uncertainty less than the dimension of the atom. It does not follow any longer that the electron will be removed from the atom by the Compton recoil, as may be seen from the following equations. It is necessary that the wave-length of the light, λ, be much less than Δq_s, or by equation (26),

$$\frac{h}{\lambda} \gg \frac{\Delta p_s}{n} .$$

The energy imparted to the electron by its recoil is approximately

$$\frac{h}{\lambda} \frac{\Delta p_s}{\mu} \gg \frac{(\Delta p_s)^2}{n\mu} \sim \frac{|E|}{n} \qquad (26a)$$

(E is the energy of the atom, μ, the mass of the electron); for large values of n, this recoil energy is much less than $|E|$, the ionization energy of the electron. On the other hand, this energy will always be great compared to the energy differences between neighboring stationary states in this region of the spectrum, which is also, in general, of the order $|E|/n$. As a matter of fact, from equation (26a) it follows at once that

$$h\nu \gg \frac{|E|}{n} ,$$

so that the frequency of the light used in making the measurement is great compared to the frequency of the electron in its orbit.

The Compton effect has as its consequence that the electron is caused to jump from a state, say $n = 1000$, to some other state for which n is, say, greater than 950 and less than 1050. The particular orbit to which the electron jumps remains essentially indeterminate because of the considerations of chapter ii, § 1b. The result of the position measurement is therefore to be represented in the mathematical scheme by a probability packet in configuration space, which is built up of characteristic functions of the states between $n=950$ and 1050. Its size is determined by the exactitude of the position measurement. This packet describes an orbit analogous to that of a corpuscle of classical mechanics, but, in general, spreads and increases in size with the time. The result of a future measurement of position can therefore only be predicted statistically. The mathematical representation of the physical process changes discontinuously with each new measurement; the observation singles out of a large number of possibilities one of which is the one which has happened. The wave packet which has spread out is replaced by a smaller one which represents the result of this observation. As our knowledge of the system does change discontinuously at each observation its mathematical representation must also change discontinuously; this is to be found in classical statistical theories as well as in the present theory.

The motion and spreading of probability packets has been studied by various authors,[1] and therefore no mathematical discussion of it need be given here. A simple consideration of Ehrenfest's[2] may be mentioned, however. Consider the motion of a single electron moving in a field of force whose potential is $V(q)$. The wave function satisfies [cf. eq. A (80)]

$$-\frac{h^2}{8\pi^2\mu}\nabla^2\psi+eV\psi=-\frac{h}{2\pi i}\frac{\partial\psi}{\partial t}, \tag{27}$$

[1] Kennard, *loc. cit.;* C. G. Darwin, *Proceedings of the Royal Society*, A, **117**, 258, 1927.

[2] P. Ehrenfest, *Zeitschrift für Physik*, **45**, 455, 1927.

and the probable value of q is given by equation (4) with $\psi = S$; q is one of the rectangular co-ordinates x, y, z. Then differentiating by t:

$$\mu\dot{\bar{q}} = \mu \int q\left(\frac{\partial\psi}{\partial t}\psi^* + \psi\frac{\partial\psi^*}{\partial t}\right) d\tau;$$

on substituting the value of $\partial\psi/\partial t$ and $\partial\psi^*/\partial t$ from (27):

$$\mu\dot{\bar{q}} = \frac{h}{4\pi}\int q(-\psi^*\nabla^2\psi + \psi\nabla^2\psi^*)d\tau\ ;$$

integrating by parts:

$$\mu\dot{\bar{q}} = \frac{h}{4\pi}\int\left(\psi^*\frac{\partial\psi}{\partial q} - \psi\frac{\partial\psi^*}{\partial q}\right)d\tau\ .$$

This process may be repeated a second time to obtain $\mu\ddot{\bar{q}}$. As the calculation is lengthy, but simple, we give only the result:

$$\mu\ddot{\bar{q}} = -e\int\frac{\partial V}{\partial q}\psi\psi^* d\tau\ . \tag{28}$$

If ψ represents a wave packet whose spatial dimension is small compared to the distance within which $\partial V/\partial q$ changes appreciably, this may be written

$$\mu\ddot{\bar{q}} = -e\frac{\partial V(\bar{q})}{\partial\bar{q}}\ . \tag{29}$$

This proves that, so long as the wave packet remains small, its center will move according to the classical equations of motion of the electron.

A remark concerning the rate of spreading of the wave packet may not be out of place at this point. If the classical motion of the system is periodic, it may happen that the size of the wave packet at first undergoes only periodic changes. The number of revolutions which the packet may perform before it spreads completely over the whole region of the atom can be calculated qualitatively as follows: If there were no spreading at all, it would be possible to make a Fourier analysis of the probability density into which only integral multiples of the fundamental frequency of the orbit enter. As a matter of fact, however, the "overtones" of quantum theory are not exactly integral multiples of this fundamental frequency. The time in which the phase of the quantum theoretical overtones is completely shifted from that of the classical overtones will be qualitatively the same as the time required for the spreading of the wave packet. Let J be the action variable of classical theory, then this time will be

$$t \sim \frac{1}{h \dfrac{\partial \nu}{\partial J}},$$

and the number of revolutions performed in this time is

$$N \sim \frac{\nu}{h \dfrac{\partial \nu}{\partial J}}. \tag{30}$$

In the special case of the harmonic oscillator, N becomes infinite—the wave packet remains small for all time. In general, however, N will be of the order of magnitude of the quantum number n.

In relation to these considerations, one other idealized experiment (due to Einstein) may be considered. We imagine a photon which is represented by a wave packet built up out of Maxwell waves.[1] It will thus have a certain spatial extension and also a certain range of frequency. By reflection at a semi-transparent mirror, it is possible to decompose it into two parts, a reflected and a transmitted packet. There is then a definite probability for finding the photon either in one part or in the other part of the divided wave packet. After a sufficient time the two parts will be separated by any distance desired; now if an experiment yields the result that the photon is, say, in the reflected part of the packet, then the probability of finding the photon in the other part of the packet immediately becomes zero. The experiment at the position of the reflected packet thus exerts a kind of action (reduction of the wave packet) at the distant point occupied by the transmitted packet, and one sees that this action is propagated with a velocity greater than that of light. However, it is also obvious that this kind of action can never be utilized for the transmission of signals so that it is not in conflict with the postulates of the theory of relativity.

d) *Energy measurements.*—The measurement of the energy of a free electron is identical with the measurement of its velocity, so that most of the possible methods have already been treated. A method not yet discussed for measuring the energy of free electrons is that in which

[1] For a single photon the configuration space has only three dimensions; the Schrödinger equation of a photon can thus be regarded as formally identical with the Maxwell equations.

they are caused to move against a retarding field. If the electron passes through the field it is customary to assume the result of classical theory, that its energy E is certainly greater than the energy V corresponding to the highest potential of the field, and if it is reflected, that its energy is smaller than this critical value. Such a conclusion is certainly incorrect in the quantum theory, and a brief discussion of the method will therefore be given here. If the width of the potential barrier is comparable to the de Broglie wave-length, λ, of the electron, a certain number of electrons will penetrate it even though their energies E are less than the critical value necessary on the classical theory. This number decreases exponentially as the width of the barrier and $V-E$ increase. Conversely, when $E>V$, a certain number will be reflected if the potential changes appreciably in a distance λ. In any practicable experiment, these conditions are not realizable, and the conclusions of the classical theory can be used without appreciable error. The mathematical treatment of the situation just sketched is important, however, and will therefore be illustrated in the case of an abrupt discontinuity in the potential distribution. The Schrödinger equation for a single electron will be used; this is not identical with the wave theory of matter, for this latter would take the reaction of the wave on itself into account. The potential distribution is shown in Figure 10. For the

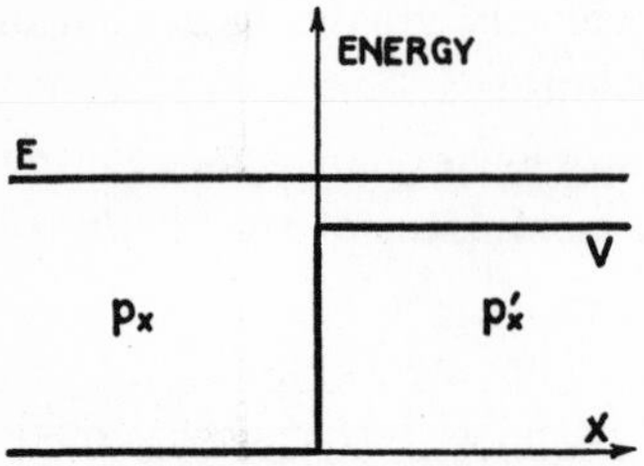

FIG. 10

incident ψ-wave in the region I ($x<0$), we then readily obtain the expression

$$\psi_i = a e^{\frac{2\pi i}{h}(px-Et)}, \qquad \frac{1}{2\mu}p^2 = E, \qquad p>0\ ; \qquad (31a)$$

for the wave penetrating into the region II ($x>0$),

$$\psi_t = a' e^{\frac{2\pi i}{h}(p'x-Et)}, \qquad \frac{1}{2\mu}p'^2 = E-V\ ; \qquad (31b)$$

and for the reflected wave in I,

$$\psi_r = a'' e^{\frac{2\pi i}{h}(-px-Et)}. \qquad (31c)$$

If p' is real, it is to be taken greater than zero; if it is imaginary, total reflection occurs and it is to be taken as positive imaginary, since ψ_t must remain finite as $x\rightarrow\infty$. At the discontinuity ($x=0$), ψ must be continuous and possess a continuous first derivative; hence

$$\left.\begin{aligned} &\psi_i+\psi_r=\psi_t \\ &\frac{\partial\psi_i}{\partial x}+\frac{\partial\psi_r}{\partial x}=\frac{\partial\psi_t}{\partial x}, \end{aligned}\right\} \text{when } x=0\ ;$$

or

$$a+a''=a'$$
$$p(a-a'')=a'p'.$$

Solving these equations for a' and a'':

$$\left.\begin{aligned} a''&=a\,\frac{p-p'}{p+p'}, \\ a'&=a\,\frac{2p}{p+p'}. \end{aligned}\right\} \qquad (32)$$

The number of electrons that pass through a given cross-section per unit time is given by the square of the absolute magnitude of the wave amplitude multiplied by the momentum provided it is real. Thus, when $E > V$, the intensities of the incident, transmitted and reflected waves are respectively proportional to

$$\left.\begin{aligned} I_i &= |a|^2 p\,; \\ I_t &= |a|^2\left(\frac{2p}{p+p'}\right)^2\,; \\ I_r &= -\,|a|^2\left(\frac{p-p'}{p+p'}\right)^2 . \end{aligned}\right\} \tag{33}$$

For imaginary values of p', the wave ψ_t does not represent a current of electrons, but a stationary charge distribution, and $I_t = 0$. As $|a''| = |a|$ in this case, $I_r = -I_i$. In both cases

$$I_i = I_t - I_r\,.$$

The relative probabilities for reflection and penetration of the electron are, by (33) and (31),

$$\left.\begin{aligned} P'' &= \frac{I_r}{I_i} = \left|\frac{\sqrt{E}-\sqrt{E-V}}{\sqrt{E}+\sqrt{E-V}}\right|^2, \\ P' &= \frac{I_t}{I_i} = \sqrt{\frac{E-V}{E}}\left|\frac{2\sqrt{E}}{\sqrt{E}+\sqrt{E-V}}\right|^2 . \end{aligned}\right\} \tag{34}$$

These expressions are plotted as solid lines in Figure 11; the curves expected from the classical theory are the dotted lines.

For the elucidation of the physical principles of the quantum theory a consideration of the mesaurement of the energy of atoms is more important than that of free electrons, and this will be given in greater detail than the preceding. As the phase of the electronic motion is the

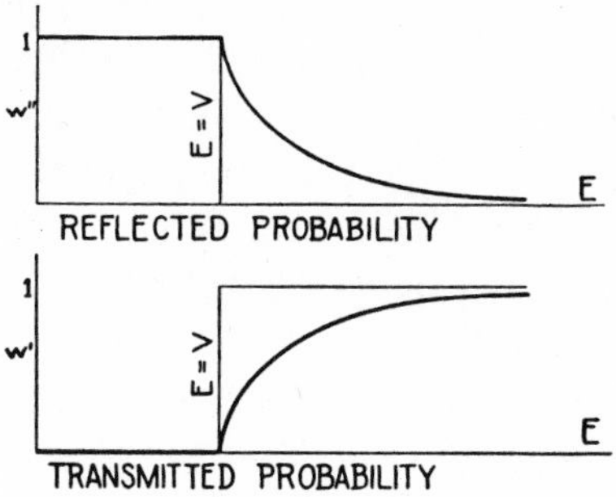

FIG. 11

variable which is canonically conjugate to the energy, it follows from the uncertainty principle that this must be completely unknown if the energy is precisely determined. Since the phase of the electronic motion determines the phase of the radiation emitted, it is this latter which is to enter the physical discussion. It will be shown that any experiment which separates atoms that are in the stationary state n from those in m necessarily destroys any pre-existing knowledge of the phase of the radiation corresponding to the transition $n \rightleftarrows m$.

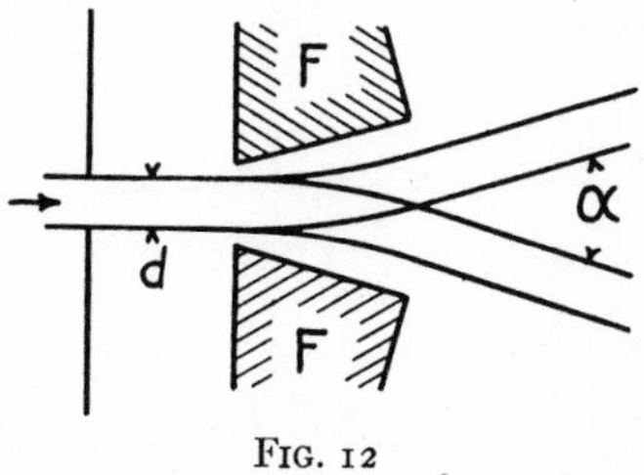

FIG. 12

Let S be a beam of atoms (Fig. 12), of width d in the x-direction, which is sent through an inhomogeneous field F (which is not necessarily a magnetic field, as in the experiment of Stern-Gerlach, but may be electric or gravitational). The energy of the atoms in state m will be designated by E_m; it will depend on the magnitude of the field F at the center of gravity of the atom, so that the deflecting force of the field in the x-direction is $\partial(E_m(F))/\partial x = (dE_m/dF)(dF/dx)$, and is different for atoms in different states. If T be the time required by the atoms to pass through the field, and p the momentum of the atoms in the direction of the beam, the angular deflection of the atoms will be

$$\frac{\partial E_m}{\partial x}\frac{T}{p}\,.$$

The original beam will thus be divided into several, each containing only atoms in one state; the angular separation a of the two beams containing atoms in states n and m, respectively, will then be

$$a=\left(\frac{\partial E_m}{\partial x}-\frac{\partial E_n}{\partial x}\right)\frac{T}{p}\,.$$

This angle must be greater than the natural scattering of the atomic beams if the two kinds of atoms are to be separated; hence

$$a\geq\frac{\lambda}{d}=\frac{h}{pd}\,. \tag{35}$$

The Schrödinger function ψ_n contains the periodic factor $e^{\frac{2\pi i}{h}E_n t}$. As E_n is a function of F, the frequency and phase of the wave are changed while passing through the field. This change is indeterminate, to a certain extent, since it is impossible to tell in what part of the beam the atom is moving and F varies from point to point. The uncertainty, $\Delta\varphi$, of the phase change of the radiation of frequency $(E_m - E_n)/h$ during the time T is therefore

$$\Delta\varphi \sim 2\pi\left(\frac{\partial E_m}{\partial x} - \frac{\partial E_n}{\partial x}\right)\frac{Td}{h} = \frac{pd}{h}\, 2\pi a\ .$$

From equation (35) it follows at once that

$$\Delta\varphi \geq 1\ . \tag{36}$$

This means complete indeterminateness in the phases.

The calculation can be carried through more concretely if it is restricted to apply only to magnetic fields. Neglecting the electron spin, it is known that the atom precesses like a rigid body when under the influence of a magnetic field H; the velocity of this precession is

$$\omega = \frac{e}{2\mu c} H\ ,$$

and its axis coincides with the direction of the field. This velocity is different for various atoms because of the width of the beam and the inhomogeneity of the field. This difference in the precession of different atoms tends to destroy any phase relation which may initially be present. For the uncertainty in ω, we readily obtain

$$\Delta\omega = \frac{ed}{2\mu c}\frac{\partial H}{\partial x}\ ,$$

and the angular separation of the two beams is

$$a = \frac{e}{2\mu c}\frac{\partial H}{\partial x}\frac{hT}{2\pi p}\ ;$$

as a must be greater than h/pd,

$$T\Delta\omega \geq 2\pi\ .$$

All trace of the original phase has thus been destroyed by the experiment. Some atoms will have executed one rotation more than others, and all intermediate angles are possible. This does not follow if the apparatus is incapable of resolving the two beams, as then α may be less than h/pd.

Bohr[1] has shown that the foregoing consideration resolves one of the paradoxes introduced by the assumption of stationary states. If a beam of atoms, all initially in the normal state, be excited to fluorescence by illumination with light of a resonance frequency, we are compelled to assume that they will radiate coherently. That is, each atom will scatter a spherical wave, whose phase is determined by that of the incident plane wave at the atom. The elementary spherical waves will then be so related that their superposition results in a refracted plane wave. From the observation of this wave it is impossible to determine the quantum state of the emitter—or even its atomic character. But if the beam leaves the illuminated region and is analyzed by means of an inhomogeneous field, only the beam of atoms in the excited state will be luminous. This beam will contain relatively few atoms, widely spaced compared to the probable length of the train of waves emitted. Their radiation must therefore be practically identical with that from independent point sources. This action of the magnetic field was quite incomprehensible as long as the assumption was retained that the resolving power of the apparatus could be increased indefinitely by decreasing the width of the beam of atoms.

[1] *Loc. cit.*

CHAPTER III

CRITIQUE OF THE PHYSICAL CONCEPTS OF THE WAVE THEORY

In the foregoing chapter the simplest concepts of the wave theory, which are well established by experiment, were assumed without question to be "correct." They were taken as the basis of a critique of the corpuscular picture, and it appeared that this picture is only applicable within certain limits, which were determined. The wave theory, as well, is only applicable with certain limitations, which will now be determined. Just as in the case of particles the limitations of a wave representation were not originally taken into account, so that historically we first encounter attempts to develop *three-dimensional* wave theories that could be readily visualized (Maxwell and de Broglie waves). For these theories the term "classical wave theories" will be used; they are related to the quantum theory of waves in the same way as classical mechanics to quantum mechanics. The mathematical scheme of the classical and quantum theories of waves will be found in the Appendix. (The reader must be warned against an unwarrantable confusion of classical wave theory with the Schrödinger theory of waves in a phase space.) After a critique of the wave concept has been added to that of the particle concept all contradictions between the two disappear—provided only that due regard is paid to the limits of applicability of the two pictures.

§ 1. THE UNCERTAINTY RELATIONS FOR WAVES

The concepts of wave amplitude, electric and magnetic field strengths, energy density, etc., were originally derived from primitive experiences of daily life, such as the observation of water waves or the vibrations of elastic bodies. These concepts are also widely applicable to light and even, as we now know, to matter waves. But since we also know that the concepts of the corpuscular theory are applicable to radiation and matter, it follows that the wave picture also has its limitations, which may be derived from the particle representation. These will now be considered, first for the case of radiation.

Before proceeding to the subject proper, however, we must first discuss briefly what is meant by an exact knowledge of a wave amplitude—for instance, that of an electric or magnetic field strength. Such an exact knowledge of the amplitude at every point of a region of space (in the strict mathematical sense) is obviously an abstraction that can never be realized. For every measurement can yield only an average value of the amplitude in a very small region of space and during a very short interval of time. Although it is perhaps possible in principle to diminish these space and time intervals without limit by refinement of the measuring instruments, nevertheless for the physical discussion of the concepts of the wave theory it is advantageous to introduce finite values for the space and time intervals involved in the measurements and only pass to the limit zero for these intervals at the end of the calculations. This is, in fact, exactly the procedure adopted in treating the mathematical theory of wave fields (cf. A, § 9). It is possible that future developments of the quantum theory will show that the limit zero for such intervals is an abstraction without physical meaning; for the present, however, there seems no reason for imposing any limitations.

For precision of thought we therefore assume that our measurements always give average values over a very small space region of volume $\delta v = (\delta l)^3$, which depends on the method of measurement. Since it is a question of the measurement of the field strengths, light of wave-length λ much less than δl will not be detected by the experiment. The measurement gives, say, the values $\boldsymbol{E}$ and $\boldsymbol{H}$ for the field strengths (averaged over δv). If these values $\boldsymbol{E}$ and $\boldsymbol{H}$ were exactly known there would be a contradiction to the particle theory, since the energy and momentum of the small volume δv are

$$E = \delta v \frac{1}{8\pi} (\boldsymbol{E}^2 + \boldsymbol{H}^2) , \qquad \boldsymbol{G} = \delta v \frac{1}{4\pi c} \boldsymbol{E} \times \boldsymbol{H} , \qquad (37)$$

and the right-hand members could be made as small as desired by taking δv sufficiently small. This is inconsistent with the particle theory, according to which the energy and momentum content of the small volume is made up of discrete and finite amounts $h\nu$ and $h\nu/c$, respectively. For the highest frequency detectable $h\nu \leq (hc/\delta l)$ so that it is clear that the right-hand members of equation (37) must be uncertain by just the magnitudes of these quanta ($h\nu$ and $h\nu/c$) in order that there be no contradiction to the particle theory. Accordingly there must be uncertainty relations between the components of $\boldsymbol{E}$ and $\boldsymbol{H}$ which give rise to an uncertainty in the value of E of the order of magnitude $hc/\delta l$ and in $\boldsymbol{G}$

of the order of magnitude $h/\delta l$ when E and G are calculated by equations (37). Let $\Delta \boldsymbol{E}$ and $\Delta \boldsymbol{H}$ be the uncertainties in $\boldsymbol{E}$ and $\boldsymbol{H}$; then the uncertainties in E and G are

$$\Delta E = \frac{\delta v}{8\pi}\{2|\boldsymbol{E}\cdot\Delta\boldsymbol{E}| + 2|\boldsymbol{H}\cdot\Delta\boldsymbol{H}| + (\Delta\boldsymbol{E})^2 + (\Delta\boldsymbol{H})^2\} ,$$

$$\Delta \boldsymbol{G}_x = \frac{\delta v}{4\pi c}\{|(\boldsymbol{E}\times\Delta\boldsymbol{H})_x| + |(\Delta\boldsymbol{E}\times\boldsymbol{H})_x| + |(\Delta\boldsymbol{E}\times\Delta\boldsymbol{H})_x|\} ,$$

with cyclic permutation for the y- and z-directions.

Since the most probable values of $\boldsymbol{E}$ and $\boldsymbol{H}$ may possibly be zero the terms on the right which contain only $\Delta\boldsymbol{E}$ and $\Delta\boldsymbol{H}$ must alone be sufficient to give the necessary uncertainty to E and $\boldsymbol{G}$. This is attained if

$$\Delta\boldsymbol{E}_x \Delta\boldsymbol{H}_y \geq \frac{hc}{\delta v \delta l} = \frac{hc}{(\delta l)^4} , \tag{38}$$

with cyclic permutation for the other components. These uncertainty relations refer to a simultaneous knowledge of $\boldsymbol{E}_x$ and $\boldsymbol{H}_y$ in the same volume element; in different volume elements $\boldsymbol{E}_x$ and $\boldsymbol{H}_y$ can be known to any degree of accuracy.

The relations (38), as in the case of the particle theory, can also be derived directly from the exchange relations for $\boldsymbol{E}$ and $\boldsymbol{H}$ (cf. A, §§ 9, 12). If a division of space into finite cells of magnitude δv is used, the integration with respect to dv in the Lagrangian of A (97) becomes a sum over all the cells δv. The momentum conjugate to $\psi_\alpha(r)$ in the rth cell is then [cf. A(104)]

$$\delta v \frac{\partial L}{\partial \dot{\psi}_\alpha(r)} = \delta v \Pi_\alpha(r) , \tag{39}$$

and in place of A(111),

$$\Pi_\alpha(r)\psi_\beta(s)-\psi_\beta(s)\Pi_\alpha(r)=\delta_{\alpha\beta}\delta_{rs}\frac{h}{2\pi i}\frac{1}{\delta v}\,, \tag{40}$$

where δ_{rs} is now the usual δ-function,

$$\delta_{rs}=\begin{cases}1 \text{ for } r=s\,,\\ 0 \text{ for } r\neq s\,.\end{cases}$$

In the limit $\delta v \to 0$ (40) becomes A(111).

From (40) and A(134) applied to the case of electric and magnetic fields it follows that

$$\boldsymbol{E}_i(r)\Phi_a(s)-\Phi_a(s)\boldsymbol{E}_i(r)=-2hci\delta_{rs}\delta_{ai}\frac{1}{\delta v}\,. \tag{41}$$

When it is remembered that an uncertainty $\Delta\Phi_k$ gives an uncertainty of order of magnitude $\Delta\Phi_k/\delta l$ for the field strengths resulting from Φ_k, it will be seen that (41) leads immediately to the uncertainty relations (38).

Matter waves may be treated in an entirely similar way. It must be noted, however, that no experiment can ever measure the amplitude directly, as is evident from the fact that the de Broglie waves are complex. If exchange relations for the wave amplitudes are derived formally from those for ψ and ψ^*, the result is, to be sure, a physically reasonable one in the case of the Bose-Einstein statistics. However, use of the experimentally correct Fermi-Dirac statistics gives the meaningless result that ψ and ψ^* cannot be exactly measured simultaneously at different points of space. It is thus highly satisfactory that there is no experiment which will measure ψ at a given point at a given time. The mathematical reason for this is that even for the interaction of radiation and matter the part of the Lagrangian referring to matter contains only terms of the form $\psi\psi^*$. From the considerations just given it can also be seen that the Bose-Einstein statistics is a physical necessity for light-quanta if one makes the apparently very natural assumption that measurements of the electric and magnetic fields at different points of space must be independent of each other.

§ 2. DISCUSSION OF AN ACTUAL MEASUREMENT OF THE ELECTROMAGNETIC FIELD

As in the case of the corpuscular picture, it must be possible to trace the origin of the uncertainty in a measurement of the electromagnetic field to its experimental

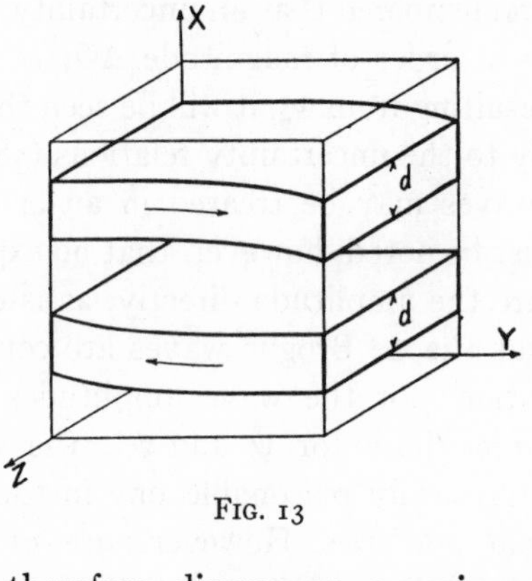

FIG. 13

source. We therefore discuss an experiment which is capable of simultaneously measuring E_x and H_z in the same element of volume δv. This can be accomplished by the observation of the deflection in the direction of x of two beams of cathode rays which traverse the volume in opposite directions along the y-axis (cf. Fig. 13). It may be assumed that the width of both beams in the z-direction is δl, i.e., the whole width of the volume element, but their widths in the perpendicular direction must be less than this, say d, so that they may traverse δv without mutual disturbance. If the distance between the two rays is of order of magnitude δl, the small inhomogeneities of the field in this direction are also averaged out; it would also be possible to vary the distance between them for this purpose. This experimental arrangement will enable the measurement of $\boldsymbol{E}_x$ and $\boldsymbol{H}_z$ in δl provided only that the fields are not too inhomogeneous; should this condition not be fulfilled, the method is incapable of giving a definite result, for the field must not vary appreciably across the width of the rays, or else these will become diffuse and no simple method of determining the deflections is then available.

The angular deflection, α, of the rays in the distance δl is to be observed, and the field can be calculated from the formulas

$$\alpha_{\pm} = \frac{e}{p_y}\left(\boldsymbol{E}_x \pm \frac{p_y}{\mu c}\boldsymbol{H}_z\right)\frac{\mu \delta l}{p_y}\ .$$

Because of the natural spreading of the matter rays, the accuracy of the measurements is given by

$$\Delta \boldsymbol{E}_x \geq \frac{h}{ed}\frac{p_y}{\mu \delta l}, \qquad \Delta \boldsymbol{H}_z \geq \frac{h}{ed}\frac{p_y}{\mu \delta l}\frac{\mu c}{p_y}. \tag{42}$$

One essential factor remains to be considered, however. Each of the two electrons which pass through δv simultaneously modifies the field, and hence the path of the other electron. The amount of this modification is uncertain to some extent, since it is not known at which point in the cathode ray the electron is to be found. The uncertainty as to the actual fields which arises from this fact is thus

$$\Delta E_x \geq \frac{ed}{(\delta l)^3}, \qquad \Delta H_z \geq \frac{ed}{(\delta l)^3}\frac{p_y}{\mu c}, \tag{43}$$

whence

$$\Delta E_x \Delta H_z \geq \frac{hc}{(\delta l)^4},$$

which was to be shown. It is to be noted that the simultaneous consideration of both the corpuscular and wave picture of the process taking place is again fundamental. If the corpuscular picture of the cathode rays had not been invoked, and a continuous distribution of charge assumed as the picture of the rays, then the uncertainty (43) would have disappeared.

CHAPTER IV

THE STATISTICAL INTERPRETATION OF QUANTUM THEORY

§ 1. MATHEMATICAL CONSIDERATIONS

It is instructive to compare the mathematical apparatus of quantum theory with that of the theory of relativity. In both cases there is an application of the theory of linear algebras. One can therefore compare the matrices of quantum theory with the symmetric tensors of the special theory of relativity. The greatest difference is the fact that the tensors of quantum theory are in a space of infinitely many dimensions, and that this space is not real but imaginary. The orthogonal transformations are replaced by the so-called "unitary" transformations. In order to obtain a picture of this space, we abstract from such differences, fundamental though they be. Then every quantum theoretical "quantity" is characterized by a tensor whose principal directions may be drawn in this space (cf. Fig. 14). In order to obtain a clear picture, one may recall the tensor of the moments of inertia of a rigid body. The principal directions are, in general, different for each quantity; only matrices which commute with one another have coincident principal directions. The exact knowledge of

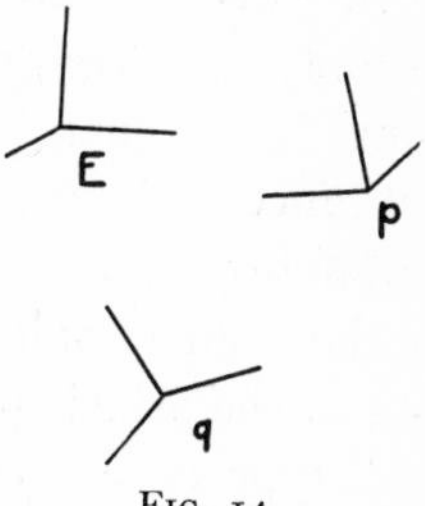

FIG. 14

the numerical value of any dynamical variable corresponds to the determination of a definite direction in this space, in the same manner as the exact knowledge of the moment of inertia of a solid body determines the principal direction to which this moment belongs (it is assumed that there is no degeneracy). This direction is thus parallel to the kth principal axis of the tensor T, along which the component T_{kk} has the value measured. The exact knowledge of the direction (except for a factor of absolute magnitude unity) in unitary space is the maximum information regarding the quantum dynamical variable which can be obtained. Weyl[1] has called this degree of knowledge a determinate case (*reiner Fall*). An atom in a (non-degenerate) stationary state presents such a determinate case: The direction characterizing it is that of the kth principal axis of the tensor E, which belongs to the energy value E_{kk}. There is obviously no significance to be attached to the terms "value of the coordinate q," etc., in this direction, just as the specification of the moment of inertia about an axis not coinciding with one of the principal directions is insufficient to determine any type of motion of the rigid body, no matter how simple. Only tensors whose principal axes coincide with those of E have a value in this direction. The total angular momentum of the atom, for example, can be determined simultaneously with its energy. If a measurement of the value of q is to be made, then the exact knowledge of the direction must be replaced by inexact information, which can be considered as a "mixture" of the original directions E_{kk}, each with a certain probability coefficient.

[1] H. Weyl, *Zeitschrift für Physik*, **46**, 1, 1927.

For example, the indeterminate recoil of the electron when its position is measured by a microscope converts the determinate case E_{kk} into such a mixture (cf. chap. ii, § 2*a*). This mixture must be of such a kind that it may also be considered as a mixture of the principal directions of q, though with other probability coefficients. The measurement singles a particular value q' out of this as being the actual result. It follows from this discussion that the value of q' cannot be uniquely predicted from the result of the experiment determining E, for a disturbance of the system, which is necessarily indeterminate to a certain degree, must occur between the two experiments involved.

This disturbance is qualitatively determined, however, as soon as one knows that the result is to be an exact value of q. In this case, the probability of finding a value q' after E has been measured is given by the square of the cosine of the angle between the original direction E_k and the direction q'. More exactly one should say by the analogue to the cosine in the unitary space, which is $|S(E_k, q')|$. This assumption is one of the formal postulates of quantum theory and cannot be derived from any other considerations. It follows from this axiom that the values of two dynamical quantities are causally related if, and only if, the tensors corresponding to them have parallel principal axes. In all other cases there is no causal relationship. The statistical relation by means of probability coefficients is determined by the disturbance of the system produced by the measuring apparatus. Unless this disturbance is produced, there is no significance to be given the terms "value" or "probable value" of a variable in a given direction of unitary space which is not parallel to a principal axis of the corresponding tensor. Thus one becomes entangled in contradictions if one speaks of the probable position of the electron without considering the experiment used to determine it (cf. the paradox of negative kinetic energy, chap. ii, § 2*d*). It must also be emphasized that the statistical character of the relation depends on the fact that the influence of the measuring device is treated in a different manner than the interaction of the various parts of the system on one another. This last interaction also causes changes in the direction of the vector representing the system in the Hilbert space, but these are completely determined. If one were to treat the measuring device as a part of the system—which would necessitate an extension of the Hilbert space—then the changes considered above as indeterminate would appear determinate. But no use could be made of this determinateness unless our observation of the measuring device were free of indeterminateness. For these observations, however, the same considerations are valid as those given above, and we should be forced, for example, to include our own eyes as part of the system, and so on. The chain of cause and effect could be quantitatively verified only if the whole universe were considered as a single system—but then physics has vanished, and only a mathematical scheme remains. The partition of the world into observing and observed system prevents a sharp formulation of the law of cause and effect. (The observing system need not always be a human being; it may also be an inanimate apparatus, such as a photographic plate.)

As examples of cases in which causal relations do exist

the following may be mentioned: The conservation theorems for energy and momentum are contained in the quantum theory, for the energies and momenta of different parts of the same system are commutative quantities. Furthermore, the principal axes of q at time t are only infinitesimally different from the principal axes of q at time $t+dt$. Hence, if two position measurements are carried out in rapid succession, it is practically certain that the electron will be in almost the same place both times.

§ 2. INTERFERENCE OF PROBABILITIES

Many paradoxical conclusions may be deduced from the foregoing principles if the perturbation introduced by measuring instruments is not adequately considered. The following idealized experiment furnishes a typical example of such a paradox.

A beam of atoms, all of which are initially in the state n, is directed through a field F_1 (Fig. 15). This field will

FIG. 15

cause transitions to other states if it is inhomogeneous in the direction of the beam, but will not separate atoms of one state from those in another. Let S'_{nm} be the transformation function for the transitions in the field F_1 so that $|S'_{nm}|^2$ is the probability of finding an atom in the state m after it has emerged from the field F_1. Farther on the atoms encounter a second field F_2, similar in properties to F_1 for which the corresponding transformation function is S''_{ml}. This field is again incapable of separating the atoms in different states, but beyond F_2 a determination of the stationary state is made by means of a third field of force. Now, for those atoms that are in the state m after passing through F_1 the probability of a transition to state l on passing F_2 is given by $|S_{ml}|^2$. Hence the probable fraction of the atoms in the state l beyond F_2 should be given by

$$\sum_m |S'_{nm}|^2 |S''_{ml}|^2 . \tag{44}$$

On the other hand, according to equation A(69), the transformation function for the combined fields F_1 and F_2 is $S'''_{nl} = \sum_m S'_{nm} S''_{ml}$, which results in the value

$$|S'''_{nl}|^2 = \left| \sum_m S'_{nm} S''_{ml} \right|^2 \tag{45}$$

for the same probability as represented by equation (44).

The contradiction disappears when it is remarked that the formulas (44) and (45) really refer to two different experiments. The reasoning leading to (44) is correct only when an experiment permitting the determination of the stationary state of the atom is performed between F_1 and F_2. The performance of such an experiment will necessarily alter the phase of the de Broglie wave of the atom in state m by an unknown amount of order of magnitude one, as has been shown in chapter ii, § 2*d*. In applying (45) to this experiment each member $S'_{nm}S''_{ml}$ in the summation must thus be multiplied by the arbitrary factor $exp(i\varphi_m)$ and then averaged over all values of φ_m. This phase average agrees with (44), which thus applies to this experiment. The rules of the calculus of probabilities can be applied to $|S_{nm}|^2$ only when the causal chain has actually been broken by an observation in the manner explained in the foregoing section. If no break of this sort has occurred it is not reasonable to speak of the atom as having been in a stationary state between F_1 and F_2, and the rules of quantum mechanics apply.

Three general cases may be illustrated by this experiment, and they must be carefully distinguished in any application of the general principles. They are:

CASE I: The atoms remain undisturbed between F_1 and F_2. The probability of observing the state l beyond F_2 is then

$$\left|\sum_m S'_{nm} S''_{ml}\right|^2 .$$

CASE II: The atoms are disturbed between F_1 and F_2 by the performance of an experiment which would have made possible the determination of the stationary state. The result of the experiment is not observed, however. The probability of the state l is then

$$\sum_m |S'_{nm}|^2 |S''_{ml}|^2 .$$

CASE III: The additional experiment of Case II is performed and its result is observed. The atom is known to have been in state m while passing from F_1 to F_2. The probability of the state l is then given by

$$|S''_{ml}|^2 .$$

The difference between Cases II and III is recognized in all treatments of the theory of probability, but the difference between I and II does not exist in classical theories which assume the possibility of observation without perturbation. When stated in a sufficiently generalized form, this distinction is the center of the whole quantum theory.

§ 3. BOHR'S CONCEPT OF COMPLEMENTARITY[1]

With the advent of Einstein's relativity theory it was necessary for the first time to recognize that the physical world differed from the ideal world conceived in terms of everyday experience. It became apparent that ordinary concepts could only be applied to processes in which the velocity of light could be regarded as practically infinite. The experimental material resulting from modern refinements in experimental technique necessitated the revision of old ideas and the acquirement of new ones, but as the mind is always slow to adjust itself to an extended range of experience and concepts, the relativity theory seemed at first repellantly abstract. None the less, the simplicity of its solution for a vexatious problem has gained it universal acceptance. As is clear from what has been said, the resolution of the paradoxes of atomic physics can be accomplished only by further renunciation of old and cherished ideas. Most important of these is the idea that natural phenomena obey exact laws—the principle of causality. In fact, our ordinary description of nature, and the idea of exact laws, rests on the assumption that it is

[1] *Nature*, **121**, 580, 1928.

possible to observe the phenomena without appreciably influencing them. To co-ordinate a definite cause to a definite effect has sense only when both can be observed without introducing a foreign element disturbing their interrelation. The law of causality, because of its very nature, can only be defined for isolated systems, and in atomic physics even approximately isolated systems cannot be observed. This might have been foreseen, for in atomic physics we are dealing with entities that are (so far as we know) ultimate and indivisible. There exist no infinitesimals by the aid of which an observation might be made without appreciable perturbation.

Second among the requirements traditionally imposed on a physical theory is that it must explain all phenomena as relations between objects existing in space and time. This requirement has suffered gradual relaxation in the course of the development of physics. Thus Faraday and Maxwell explained electromagnetic phenomena as the stresses and strains of an ether, but with the advent of the relativity theory, this ether was dematerialized; the electromagnetic field could still be represented as a set of vectors in space-time, however. Thermodynamics is an even better example of a theory whose variables cannot be given a simple geometric interpretation. Now, as a geometric or kinematic description of a process implies observation, it follows that such a description of atomic processes necessarily precludes the exact validity of the law of causality—and conversely. Bohr[1] has pointed out that it is therefore impossible to demand that both require-

[1] *Ibid.*

ments be fulfilled by the quantum theory. They represent complementary and mutually exclusive aspects of atomic phenomena. This situation is clearly reflected in the theory which has been developed. There exists a body of exact mathematical laws, but these cannot be interpreted as expressing simple relationships between objects existing in space and time. The observable predictions of this theory can be approximately described in such terms, but not uniquely—the wave and the corpuscular pictures both possess the same approximate validity. This indeterminateness of the picture of the process is a direct result of the interdeterminateness of the concept "observation"—it is not possible to decide, other than arbitrarily, what objects are to be considered as part of the observed system and what as part of the observer's apparatus. In the formulas of the theory this arbitrariness often makes it possible to use quite different analytical methods for the treatment of a single physical experiment. Some examples of this will be given later. Even when this arbitrariness is taken into account the concept "observation" belongs, strictly speaking, to the class of ideas borrowed from the experiences of everyday life.[1] It can only be carried over to atomic phenomena when due regard is paid to the limitations placed on all space-time descriptions by the uncertainty principle.

The general relationships discussed here may be summarized in the following[2] diagrammatic form:

[1] It need scarcely be remarked that the term "observation" as here used does not refer to the observation of lines on photographic plates, etc., but rather to the observation of "the electrons in a single atom," etc. Cf. p. 1.

[2] N. Bohr, *loc. cit.*

CLASSICAL THEORY

CAUSAL RELATIONSHIPS OF PHENOMENA DESCRIBED IN TERMS OF SPACE AND TIME

QUANTUM THEORY

Either		*Or*
Phenomena described in terms of space and time *But* Uncertainty principle	Alternatives related statistically	Causal relationship expressed by mathematical laws *But* Physical description of phenomena in space-time impossible

It is only after attempting to fit this fundamental complementarity of space-time description and causality into one's conceptual scheme that one is in a position to judge the degree of consistency of the methods of quantum theory (particularly of the transformation theory). To mold our thoughts and language to agree with the observed facts of atomic physics is a very difficult task, as it was in the case of the relativity theory. In the case of the latter, it proved advantageous to return to the older philosophical discussions of the problems of space and time. In the same way it is now profitable to review the fundamental discussions, so important for epistemology, of the difficulty of separating the subjective and objective aspects of the world. Many of the abstractions that are characteristic of modern theoretical physics are to be found discussed in the philosophy of past centuries. At that time these abstractions could be disregarded as mere mental exercises by those scientists whose only concern was with reality, but today we are compelled by the refinements of experimental art to consider them seriously.

CHAPTER V

DISCUSSION OF IMPORTANT EXPERIMENTS

In the preceding chapters the principles of the quantum theory have all been discussed, but a real understanding of them is obtainable only through their relation to the body of experimental facts which the theory must explain. This is particularly true of the general principle of complementarity. A discussion of further experiments of a less idealized type than those previously used to illustrate the separate principles is therefore necessary at this point.

§ 1. THE C. T. R. WILSON EXPERIMENTS

The essential features of the C. T. R. Wilson photographs may be most easily explained with the help of the classical corpuscular picture. This explanation is also completely justified from the standpoint of the quantum theory. The uncertainty relations are not essential to the explanation of the primary fact of the rectilinearity of the tracks of α-particles. It is always correct to apply the classical theory to such semi-macroscopic phenomena, and the quantum theory is necessary only for the explanation of the finer features.

Nevertheless it will be profitable to discuss the quantum theory of the Wilson photograph. We encounter at once the arbitrariness in the concept of observation already mentioned, and it appears purely as a matter of expediency whether the molecules to be ionized are regarded as belonging to the observed system or to the observing apparatus. Consider first the latter alternative. The system to be observed then consists of one α-particle only, and the position measurement resulting from the ionization will be represented in the mathematical scheme of the theory by a probability packet $|\psi(q')|^2$ in the co-ordinate space $q=x, y, z$, of the α-particle. The calculation will be carried out only for one of the three degrees of freedom.

If the time of this determination be taken as $t=0$, and if a previous determination at a known time is also available, the momentum of the particle at time $t=0$ may be determined: let $\bar{p}$ and $\bar{q}$ denote the most probable values of the momentum and co-ordinate at this time, and Δp, Δq the probable errors. The value of the uncertainty product will be considerably greater than h in any actual case, but we may assume that $\Delta p \Delta q = h/2\pi$ (cf. the remarks concerning scintillation measurements, chap. ii, § 2*a*). This is a determinate case; it is then known [eq. (15)] that

$$\psi(q_0') = e^{-(q_0'-\bar{q})^2/2(\Delta q)^2 - \frac{2\pi i}{h}\bar{p}(q'-\bar{q})} .$$

(The index 0 indicates that q_0' is the value of the co-ordinate at $t=0$.) The quantum theoretical equations of motion are then

$$p = p_0 = \text{Const.},$$

$$\dot{q} = \frac{1}{\mu} p .$$

Although p and q do not commute, the latter equation may nevertheless be integrated[1] to

$$q=\frac{1}{\mu}pt+q_0 .$$

To obtain the probability amplitude $\psi(q')$ at time t the transformation function must be calculated from A(41) and A(42):

$$\left(\frac{t}{\mu}\frac{h}{2\pi i}\frac{\partial}{\partial q_0'}+q_0'\right)S(q_0'q')=q'S(q_0'q') .$$

The solution of this equation is

$$S(q_0'q')=ae^{\frac{2\pi i\mu}{ht}(q'q_0'-q_0'^2/2)} ; \tag{46}$$

by A(69) the distribution at time t is then to be found from

$$\psi(q')=\int_{-\infty}^{+\infty}\psi(q_0')S(q_0'q')dq_0' ,$$

which becomes, on evaluation of the integral,

$$\psi(q')=be^{[\bar{q}+i(q'-\bar{p}t/\mu)]^2/[2(\Delta q)^2(1+i/\beta)]} , \tag{47}$$

where

$$\beta=\frac{h}{2\pi}\frac{t}{\mu}\frac{1}{(\Delta q)^2}=\Delta p\frac{t}{\mu\Delta q} .$$

It follows that

$$|\psi(q')|^2=b'e^{-(q'-p't/\mu-\bar{q})^2/[(\Delta q)^2+(t\Delta p/\mu)^2]} . \tag{48}$$

[1] Kennard, *Zeitschrift für Physik*, 44, 326, 1927.

The most probable value for q' is thus $(t/\mu)\bar{p}+\bar{q}$, which is the result to be expected on the classical theory. The mean square error $(\Delta q)^2+(t\Delta p/\mu)^2$ for q' is made up of two terms corresponding to the uncertainties in q_0' and p_0'; its value again agrees with that which would be calculated classically.

If these methods are applied to all three degrees of freedom, x, y, z, it is seen at once that the path of the center of the probability packet is a straight line. It is to be noted, however, that this result applies only while the α-particle is undisturbed in its motion. Each successive ionization of a water molecule transforms the packet (48) into an aggregate of such packets (Case II, p. 61). If the ionization is accompanied by an observation of the position, a smaller probability packet of the same form as (48) but with new parameters is separated out of the aggregate (Case III, p. 61). This forms the starting-point of a new orbit—and so on. The angular deviations between successive orbital segments are determined by the relative momenta of the particle and the atomic electron with which it interacts, which accounts for the differences between the paths of α- and β-particles.

As regards the formal aspect of the foregoing calculations, it may be noted that the transformation from q_0' to q' can also be carried out by way of the energy. By equation A(70):

$$S(q_0'q')=\int S(q_0'E)S(Eq')dE \; ,$$

and therefore

$$\psi(q')=\int S(Eq')dE\int\psi(q_0')S(q_0'E)dq_0' \; .$$

The functions $S(q'E)$, $S(Eq'_0)$ are the normalized Schrödinger wave functions for the free electron; the function $\psi(q')$ can thus be built up by superposition of such Schrödinger functions. This method has been used by Darwin in an investigation of the motion of probability packets.

To complete this discussion we shall finally carry through a mathematical treatment of the Wilson photographs under the assumption that the molecules to be ionized are regarded as part of the system. This procedure is more complicated than the preceding method, but has the advantage that the discontinuous change of the probability function recedes one step and seems less in conflict with intuitive ideas. In order to avoid complication we consider only two molecules and one α-particle, and suppose the centers of mass of the former to be fixed at the points $x_1, y_1, z_1; x_2, y_2, z_2$. The α-particle is in motion with the momenta p_x, p_y, p_z, and its co-ordinates are x, y, z. The co-ordinates of the electrons in the molecules may be denoted by the single symbols q_1 and q_2, respectively; the configuration space will thus involve only x, y, z, q_1, and q_2. We inquire for the probability that both molecules will be ionized and show that it is negligibly small unless the line joining them has nearly the same direction as the vector $(p_x p_y p_z)$. All interaction between the two molecules will be neglected, and their interaction with the α-particle will be treated as a perturbation;[1] the energy of this interaction may be written

$$\left.\begin{aligned} H^{(1)}(1)+H^{(1)}(2)=H^{(1)}&(x-x_1,\ y-y_1,\ z-z_1,\ q_1) \\ &+H^{(1)}(x-x_2,\ y-y_2,\ z-z_2,\ q_2)\ , \end{aligned}\right\} \quad (49)$$

[1] M. Born, *Zeitschrift für Physik*, **38**, 803, 1926.

regarded as operators acting on the Schrödinger function. The wave equation is then

$$\left.\begin{array}{l}\underbrace{-\frac{h^2}{8\pi^2\mu}\nabla^2\psi}_{\alpha\text{-Particle}}+\underbrace{H^0(q_1)\psi+H^0(q_2)\psi}_{\text{Molecules}}+\underbrace{\epsilon[H^{(1)}(1)+H^{(1)}(2)]\psi}_{\text{Interaction}}\\ \qquad\qquad\qquad\qquad\qquad\qquad+\frac{h}{2\pi i}\frac{\partial\psi}{\partial t}=0\,,\end{array}\right\} \quad (50)$$

in which $\nabla^2=\partial^2/\partial x^2+\partial^2/\partial y^2+\partial^2/\partial z^2$, $H^0(q_i)$ is the energy operator of the molecule i, and ϵ is the perturbation parameter in powers of which the wave function is to be expanded: $\psi=\psi^{(0)}+\epsilon\psi^{(1)}+\epsilon^2\psi^{(2)}.\ .\ .\ .\ .$ Substituting this series into the wave equation and equating each power of ϵ to zero, we obtain

$$\left.\begin{array}{l}-\frac{h^2}{8\pi^2\mu}\nabla^2\psi^{(0)}+H^{(0)}(1)\psi^{(0)}+H^{(0)}(2)\psi^{(0)}+\frac{h}{2\pi i}\frac{\partial\psi^{(0)}}{\partial t}\\ \qquad\qquad=0\,,\\ -\frac{h^2}{8\pi^2\mu}\nabla^2\psi^{(1)}+H^{(0)}(1)\psi^{(1)}+H^{(0)}(2)\psi^{(1)}+\frac{h}{2\pi i}\frac{\partial\psi^{(1)}}{\partial t}\\ \qquad\qquad=-[H^{(1)}(1)+H^{(1)}(2)]\psi^{(0)}\,,\\ -\frac{h^2}{8\pi^2\mu}\nabla^2\psi^{(2)}+H^{(0)}(1)\psi^{(2)}+H^{(0)}(2)\psi^{(2)}+\frac{h}{2\pi i}\frac{\partial\psi^{(2)}}{\partial t}\\ \qquad\qquad=-[H^{(1)}(1)+H^{(1)}(2)]\psi^{(1)}\,,\\ .\end{array}\right\} \quad (51)$$

The characteristic solutions of the first equation are

$$\psi^{(0)}=e^{\frac{2\pi i}{h}\boldsymbol{p}\cdot\boldsymbol{x}}\varphi_{n_1}(q_1)\varphi_{n_2}(q_2)e^{-\frac{2\pi i}{h}E^{(0)}t}\,, \qquad (52)$$

where

$$H^{(0)}(q)\varphi_n(q)=E_n\varphi_n(q) \ , \tag{53}$$

and

$$E^0=\frac{1}{2\mu}\,p^2+E_{n_1}+E_{n_2} \, . \tag{54}$$

These solutions correspond to the case in which the momentum of the α-particle is known to be exactly p, its position therefore entirely unknown, while the molecules are known to be in the states n_1, n_2, respectively. All interaction is neglected, and the problem is to determine how the interaction modifies this state of affairs.

This may be solved by determining $\psi^{(1)}$, $\psi^{(2)}$ according to the method of Born. These quantities are first expanded in terms of the orthogonal functions $\varphi_{m_1}(q_1)$ $\varphi_{m_2}(q_2)$,

$$\psi^{(i)}=\sum_{m_1}\sum_{m_2} v^{(i)}_{m_1 m_2}\,\varphi_{m_1}(q_1)\,\varphi_{m_2}(q_2) \ , \tag{55}$$

in which the $v^{(i)}_{m_1 m_2}$ are of course functions of x, y, z, and t. The significance of these quantities is that

$$\left|\sum_i \epsilon^i v^{(i)}_{m_1 m_2}\right|^2 \tag{56}$$

is the probability of observing the molecule 1 in the state m_1, molecule 2 in the state m_2, and the electron at x, y, z.

Substituting equation (55) for $i=1$ into the first of equations (51), we obtain

$$\left(-\frac{h^2}{8\pi^2\mu}\,\nabla^2+E_{n_1}+E_{n_2}+\frac{h}{2\pi i}\,\frac{\partial}{\partial t}\right)v^{(1)}_{n_1 m_2}$$

$$=-[h_{n_1 m_2}(1)\delta_{n_2 m_2}+h_{n_2 m_2}(2)\delta_{n_1 m_1}]e^{\frac{2\pi i}{h}[p\cdot x-E^0 t]} \ ,$$

in which the abbreviations

$$\left.\begin{aligned} h_{n_1m_1}(1) &= \int \varphi^*_{m_1}(q_1) H^{(1)}(1) \varphi_{n_1}(q_1) dq_1 \\ h_{n_2m_2}(2) &= \int \varphi^*_{m_2}(q_2) H^{(1)}(2) \varphi_{n_2}(q_2) dq_2 \end{aligned}\right\} \qquad (57)$$

have been used. The co-ordinates q_1 and q_2 have thus been eliminated from further consideration; the functions $h(1)$, $h(2)$ are functions of x, y, z, and of x_1, y_1, z_1 or x_2, y_2, z_2, respectively. These equations may be further simplified by writing

$$v^{(1)}_{m_1m_2}(xyzt) = w^{(1)}_{m_1m_2}(xyz) e^{-\frac{2\pi i}{h} E^0 t} ,$$

whence

$$(\nabla^2 + k^2_{m_1m_2}) w^{(1)}_{m_1m_2} = \frac{8\pi^2\mu}{h^2} \left(h_{n_1m_1}(1) \delta_{n_2m_2} + h_{n_2m_2}(2) \delta_{n_1m_1} \right) e^{\frac{2\pi i}{h} \mathbf{p \cdot x}} \qquad (58)$$

where

$$\frac{h^2}{8\pi^2\mu} k^2_{m_1m_2} = \left[E_{n_1} + E_{n_2} + \frac{1}{2\mu} p^2 - E_{m_1} - E_{m_2} \right] . \qquad (59)$$

In this expression the kinetic energy of the α-particle is so much greater than the other terms that, to a sufficient approximation, we may take

$$k^2_{m_1m_2} = k^2 = \frac{4\pi^2 p^2}{h^2} = \frac{4\pi^2}{\lambda_0^2} . \qquad (60)$$

Equations (58) are then all of the form

$$(\nabla^2 + k^2) w^{(1)}_{m_1m_2} = \rho_{m_1m_2}(xyz) , \qquad (61)$$

which is the ordinary equation of wave-motion; $\rho_{m_1m_2}(xyz)$ is the density of the oscillators producing the wave, and, as it is complex, also determines their phase. The solution of equation (61) is given by Huyghen's principle:

$$w^{(1)}_{m_1m_2}=\iiint\rho_{m_1m_2}(x'y'z')\,\frac{e^{-ikR}}{R}\,dx'dy'dz'\ ,$$

where R is the distance from x', y', z' to x, y, z.

Since, according to (58), $\rho_{m_1m_2}$ is zero unless $m_1=n_1$ or $m_2=n_2$, all the $w^{(1)}_{m_1m_2}$ will be zero except $w^{(1)}_{m_1n_2}$ and $w^{(1)}_{n_1m_2}$; to the first approximation, only one of the two

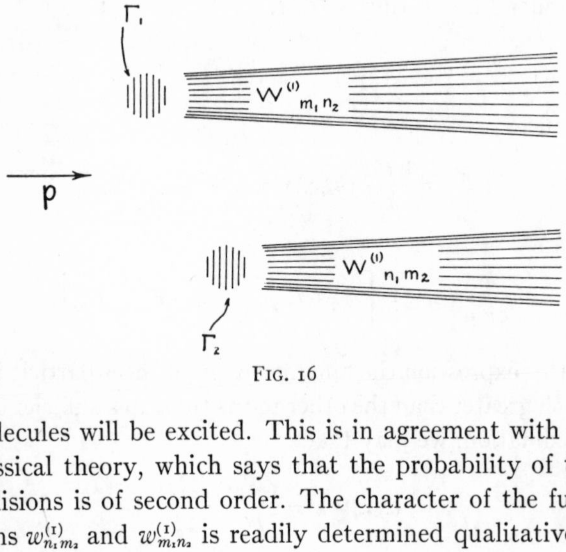

FIG. 16

molecules will be excited. This is in agreement with the classical theory, which says that the probability of two collisions is of second order. The character of the functions $w^{(1)}_{n_1m_2}$ and $w^{(1)}_{m_1n_2}$ is readily determined qualitatively; by equation (57)

$$\rho_{m_1n_2}=\frac{8\pi^2\mu}{h^2}\,h_{n_2m_1}(x-x_1,\ y-y_1,\ z-z_1)e^{\frac{2\pi i}{h}\mathbf{p}\cdot\mathbf{x}}\ .$$

The (fictitious) oscillators producing the wave are thus all located in the region Γ_1 about x_1, y_1, z_1 (cf. Fig. 16) in which $h_{n_2m_1}$ is appreciably different from zero. They vibrate coherently, their phase being determined essentially by the factor $e^{\frac{2\pi i}{h}\mathbf{p}\cdot\mathbf{x}}$; in the figure the lines of equal phase are drawn perpendicular to p. They are spaced at distances λ_0. According to equation (61) the wave-length emitted by the oscillators is also λ_0, and a simple application of Huyghen's principle shows that the wave disturbance will have an appreciable amplitude only in the conical region which is shaded and whose axis is in the direction of $\mathbf{p}$. The cross-section of this region near x_1, y_1, z_1 is determined by the cross-section of the molecule: Γ_1. Its angular opening also depends on Γ_1, being greater when Γ_1 is small—i.e., the uncertainty relation $\Delta p_x \Delta x \sim h/2\pi$ is fulfilled. Similar considerations apply to $w^{(1)}_{n_1m_2}$; it is different from zero only in a beam originating in Γ_2 and also having the direction $\mathbf{p}$.

We now pass to the second approximation: $v^{(2)}_{m_1m_2}$ may also be written $w^{(2)}_{m_1m_2} exp(-2\pi i/h)\, E^0 t$ and equation (51) reduces to

$$\left.\begin{aligned}(\nabla^2+k^2)w^{(2)}_{m_1m_2} &= \frac{8\pi^2\mu}{h^2}\left\{\sum_l w^{(1)}_{lm_2}h_{lm_1}(1)+\sum_l w^{(1)}_{m_1l}h_{m_2l}(2)\right\},\\ &= \frac{8\pi^2\mu}{h^2}\{w^{(1)}_{n_1m_2}h_{n_1m_1}(1)+w^{(1)}_{m_1n_2}h_{m_2n_2}(2)\}\,.\end{aligned}\right\}\quad(62)$$

The right-hand side of this equation will always be practically zero unless one of the two molecules lies in the beam originating at the other, for $w^{(1)}_{n_1m_2}$ is different from zero only in the beam originating in Γ_2 and $h_{n_1m_1}(1)$ only in Γ_1. Unless these two regions intersect, the first term will be zero; similarly the second term. Thus the probability of simultaneous ionization or excitation of the two atoms will vanish even in the second approximation unless the line joining their centers of gravity is practically parallel to the direction of motion of the α-particle. These considerations may be extended to the case of any number of molecules without essential modification. For each additional molecule the approximation must be carried one step farther, but the principles and results will be the same. It has thus been proved that the ionized molecules will lie practically on straight lines, and that the deviations from rectilinearity satisfy the uncertainty relations. In thus including the molecules in the observed system, it has not been necessary to introduce the discontinuously changing probability packet, but if we wish to consider the methods by which the excitation of the molecule can actually be observed, these discontinuous changes (now of a probability packet in the configuration space x, y, z, q_1, q_2) will again play a rôle.

§ 2. DIFFRACTION EXPERIMENTS

The diffraction of light or matter (Davisson-Germer, Thomson, Rupp, Kikuchi) by gratings may be explained most simply by the aid of the classical wave theories. The application of space-time wave theories to these experiments is justified from the point of view of the quantum theory, since the uncertainty relations do not in any way affect the purely geometrical aspects of the waves, but only their amplitude (cf. chap. iii, § 1). The quantum theory need only be invoked when discussing the dynamical relations involving the energy and momentum content of the waves.

The quantum theory of the waves being thus certainly in agreement with the classical theory in so far as the geometric diffraction pattern is concerned, it seems useless to prove it by detailed calculation. On the other hand, Duane has given an interesting treatment of diffraction phenomena from the quantum theory of the corpuscular picture. We imagine for simplicity that the corpuscle is reflected from a plane ruled grating, whose constant is d.

Let the grating itself be movable. Its translation in the x-direction may be looked upon as a periodic motion, in so far as only the interaction of the incident particles with the grating is considered; for the displacement of the whole grating by an amount d will not change this interaction. Thus we may conclude that the motion of the grating in this direction is quantized and that its momentum p_x may assume only the values nh/d (as follows at once from the earlier form of the theory: $\int pdq = nh$). Since the total momentum of grating and particle must remain unchanged, the momentum of the particle can be changed only by an amount mh/d (m an integer):

$$p_x' = p_x + \frac{mh}{d} .$$

Furthermore, because of its large mass, the grating cannot take up any appreciable amount of energy, so that

$$p_x'^2 + p_y'^2 = p_x^2 + p_y^2 = p^2 .$$

If θ is the angle of incidence, θ' that of reflection, we have

$$\cos\theta = \frac{p_y}{p} , \qquad \cos\theta' = \frac{p_y'}{p} ,$$

whence

$$\sin\theta' - \sin\theta = \frac{mh}{pd} \ .$$

From equation A(83) for the wave-length of the wave associated with a particle it then follows that

$$d(\sin\theta' - \sin\theta) = m\lambda \ ,$$

in agreement with the ordinary wave theory.

The dual characters of both matter and light gave rise to many difficulties before the physical principles involved were clearly comprehended, and the following paradox was often discussed. The forces between a part of the grating and the particle certainly diminish very rapidly with the distance between the two. The direction of reflection should therefore be determined only by those parts of the grating which are in the immediate neighborhood of the incident particle, but none the less it is found that the most widely separated portions of the grating are the important factors in determining the sharpness of the diffraction maxima. The source of this contradiction is the confusion of two different experiments (Cases I and II, p. 61). If no experiment is performed which would permit the determination of the position of the particle before its reflection, there is no contradiction with observation if the whole of the grating does act on it. If, on the other hand, an experiment is performed which determines that the particle will strike on a section of length Δx of the grating, it must render the knowledge of the particle's momentum essentially uncertain by an amount $\Delta p \sim h/\Delta x$. The direction of its reflection will therefore become correspondingly uncertain. The numerical value of this uncertainty in direction is precisely that which would be calculated from the resolving power of a grating of $\Delta x/d$ lines. If $\Delta x \ll d$ the interference maxima disappear entirely; not until this case is reached can the path of the particle properly be compared with that expected on the classical particle theory, for not until then can it be determined whether the particle will impinge on a ruling or on one of the plane parts of the surface, etc.

§ 3. THE EXPERIMENT OF EINSTEIN AND RUPP[1]

Another paradox was thought to be presented by the following experiment: An atom (canal ray) is made to pass a slit S of width d with the velocity v, and emits light while doing so. This light is analyzed by a spectroscope behind S. Since the light can reach the spectroscope only during the time $t=d/v$, the train of waves to be analyzed has a finite length, and the spectroscope will show it as a line whose width corresponds to a frequency range

$$\Delta\nu=\frac{1}{t}=\frac{v}{d}\,.$$

On the other hand, the corpuscular theory seems to prohibit such a broadening. The atom emits monochromatic radiation, the energy of each particle of which is $h\nu$, and the diaphragm (because of its great mass) will not be able to change the energy of the particles.

The fallacy lies in neglecting the Doppler effect and the diffraction of the light at the slit. Those photons which reach P from the atom are not all emitted perpendicularly

[1] A. Einstein, *Berliner Berichte*, p. 334, 1926; A. Rupp, *ibid.*, p. 341, 1926.

to the canal ray; the angular aperture of the beam of photons is $\sin \alpha \sim \lambda/d$ because of the diffraction. The Doppler change of frequency due to this is

$$\Delta\nu = \sin \alpha \, \frac{v}{c} \, \nu \, ,$$

or

$$\Delta\nu = \frac{\lambda v}{cd} \, \nu = \frac{v}{d} \, ,$$

in agreement with the previous result. In this experiment the exact validity of the energy law for corpuscles is thus in conformity with the requirements of classical optics.

§ 4. EMISSION, ABSORPTION, AND DISPERSION OF RADIATION

a) *Application of the conservation laws.*—The postulate of the existence of stationary states, combined with the theory of photons, is sufficient to give a qualitative explanation of the interaction of atoms and radiation. This was the first decisive success of the Bohr theory. The most important results of this theory may be briefly summarized here. Let the stationary states of the atom be numbered 1, 2, 3 . . . . n . . . . (Fig. 17), counting from the normal state. An atom in state 3, for example, can spontaneously perform a transition to state 2, and emit a photon of energy $h\nu_{32} = E_3 - E_2$. In the

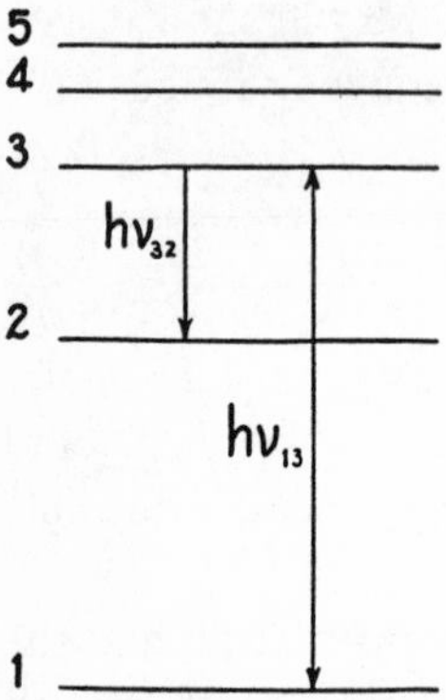

Fig. 17

same way, an atom in state 1 may absorb a photon of energy $h\nu_{31}=E_3-E_1$ and thus be excited to the state 3. It must be emphasized that these statements are to be taken quite literally, and not as having only a symbolic significance, for it is possible (e.g., by a Stern-Gerlach experiment) to determine the stationary state of the atoms both before and after the emission. It therefore follows that the intensity of an emission line is proportional to the number of atoms in the upper of the two states associated with it, while the intensity of an absorption line is proportional to the number of atoms in the lower state. These results, which have certainly been amply confirmed by experiment, are entirely characteristic of the quantum theory and can be deduced from no classical theory, either of the wave or particle representation, since even the existence of discrete energy values can never be explained by the classical theory.

An exactly similar situation is met with in the case of scattering. If an atom in state 1 is excited by a photon $h\nu$ it can re-emit the same light quantum without change of state (the mass of the nucleus being assumed infinite), or it can send out the light quantum of energy $h\nu'=h\nu-E_2+E_1$ by transition to state 2 (Smekal[1] transition; see Fig. 18). The intensity of both kinds of scattered light is proportional to the number of atoms in state 1. If an atom in state 2 is irradiated with light of frequency ν it can emit a photon of energy $h\nu'=h\nu+E_2-E_1$ of shorter wave-length by transition to state 1, and again the intensity of this "anti-Stokes" scattered light is propor-

[1] *Naturwissenschaften*, 11, 873, 1923.

tional to the number of atoms in state 2. This has been confirmed by Raman's[1] experiments.

b) *Correspondence principle and the method of virtual charges.*—The postulate of stationary states and the theory of photons, because of their very nature, cannot yield any information either regarding the interference of the emitted light or even regarding the a priori probability of the transitions involved. The interference properties can be completely accounted for by the classical wave theory, but it is in turn unable to account for the transitions. To treat these successfully a self-consistent quantum theory of radiation is necessary. It is true that an ingenious combination of arguments based on the correspondence principle can make the quantum theory of matter together with a classical theory of radiation furnish quantitative values for the transition probabilities, i.e., either by the use of Schrödinger's virtual charge density or its equivalent, the element of the matrix representing the electric dipole moment of the atom. Such a formulation of the radiation problem is far from satisfactory, however, and easily leads to false conclusions. These

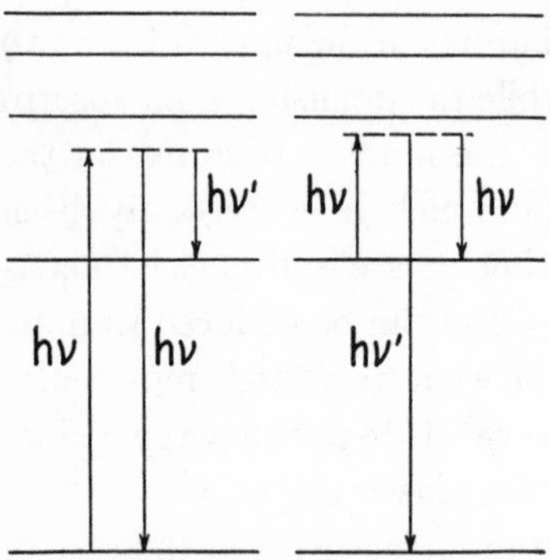

Fig. 18

[1] *Nature*, **121**, 501; **122**, 12, 1928.

methods may only be applied with the greatest caution, as the following examples may illustrate.

Consider first the case of an atom containing a single electron, and whose nucleus has an infinite mass. If $x \equiv (x, y, z)$ be the co-ordinate of the electron, and $\psi_0(x)$ the Schrödinger function, then

$$-ex_{nm} = -e\int x\psi_n\psi_m^* d\tau \tag{63}$$

is the element of the matrix representing the dipole moment of the atom. This matrix can enter, strictly speaking, only into calculations based on the principles of the quantum theory of the electron, which in no way involve radiation. It may none the less be interpreted as the dipole moment of the virtual oscillator producing the radiation which is emitted during the transition $n \rightarrow m$. This may be deduced from the correspondence principle by remembering that it has been shown that $x_{nm} \rightarrow x_n(n-m)$ in the limit of large quantum numbers, where $x_n(n-m)$ is a Fourier coefficient of the classical motion. It may thus be presumed that x_{nm} will enter into the formulas determining the intensity of the radiation in the same way as $x_n(n-m)$, i.e., that $|x_{nm}|^2$ will be the a priori probability of the transition $n \rightarrow m$. It must be emphasized that this is a purely formal result; it does not follow from any of the physical principles of quantum theory.

It may be made plausible by another consideration which brings out its unsatisfactory character more clearly. It has been pointed out that the solutions ψ_n of the Schrödinger equation are first approximations to the solutions of the classical matter-wave equations [cf. A(8)]. Denoting by ψ^c a true solution of the latter, the radiation from the charge distribution thus represented will be determined by its dipole moment

$$-e\int\psi^c\psi^{c*}x\,d\tau$$

provided the extension of this distribution is small compared to the wave-length of the radiation emitted. Now

$$\psi^c \sim \sum_n a_n\psi_n e^{-\frac{2\pi i}{h}E_n t},$$

whence the radiation, calculated by means of this classical distribution, should be determined by

$$-e\sum_{nm} a_n a_m^* x_{nm} e^{\frac{2\pi i}{h}(E_n - E_m)t}\,. \tag{64}$$

This formula is certainly wrong since it is derived from a purely classical theory; the intensity of the radiation of frequency $(E_n - E_m)/n$ depends on the coefficient a_m of the final state, as well as on a_n of the initial state. This is in direct contradiction to Bohr's fundamental postulate. The contradiction may be eliminated by arbitrarily dissecting the sum into its separate terms, omitting the offending factors and relating each term to the upper level. The formula (63) for the moment of the virtual dipole associated with the transition then appears once more.

c) The complete treatment of radiation and matter.—The consistent treatment of radiation phenomena requires the simultaneous application of the quantum theory to radiation and matter, in which case it is naturally immaterial whether the particle or wave representation is used.

Dirac,[1] in his radiation theory, employs the language of the particle representation, but makes use of conclusions drawn from the wave theory of radiation in his derivation of the Hamiltonian function. The fundamental ideas of this theory are briefly outlined here.

The atom will be represented by a single electron moving in an electrostatic force field ϕ_0. The relativistically invariant equation of the one electron problem is, according to Dirac[2] (ϕ_0 scalar potential, ϕ_i $[i=1, 2, 3]$, electromagnetic potentials),

$$p_0+\frac{e}{c}\phi_0+\alpha_i\left(p_i+\frac{e}{c}\phi_i\right)+\alpha_4 mc=0\,, \qquad (65)$$

or

$$H=-e\phi_0-\alpha_i c\left(p_i+\frac{e}{c}\phi_i\right)-\alpha_4 mc^2\,. \qquad (66)$$

(The usual summation convention is adopted.) Here, as before, the p_i's are the momenta canonically conjugate to the q_i, and the α's are operators which satisfy the equations

$$\alpha_i\alpha_k+\alpha_k\alpha_i=2\delta_{ik}\,;\quad \alpha_i\alpha_4+\alpha_4\alpha_i=0\,;\quad \alpha_4^2=1\,. \qquad (67)$$

From the equations of motion it follows that

$$\dot{p}_i=-\frac{\partial H}{\partial q_i}=\alpha_k c\,\frac{\partial \phi_k}{\partial x_i}\,;\quad \dot{q}_i=\frac{\partial H}{\partial p_i}=-\alpha_i c\,. \qquad (68)$$

Except for a factor $(-c)$ the α_i's are thus identical with the velocity matrices. From (66) it follows that the inter-

[1] *Proceedings of the Royal Society*, A, **114**, 243, 710, 1927.

[2] *Ibid.*, **117**, 610, 1928.

action energy of atoms and radiation field can be written in the simple form

$$-a_i e\phi_i = \frac{e}{c}\dot{q}_i\phi_i \ . \tag{69}$$

The Hamiltonian function of the complete system atom plus radiation field is thus

$$H_{total\ system} = H_{atom} + \frac{e}{c}\dot{q}_i\phi_i + H_{radiation\ field} \tag{70}$$

The problem is brought into a simple mathematical form by assuming the radiation field to be in an inclosure, thus providing an orthogonal system of functions on solution of the Maxwell equations subject to the appropriate boundary conditions. The ϕ_i may be developed in this system, and the coefficients [cf. A(123) and (124)] may be written in the form

$$a_r = e^{-\frac{2\pi i}{h}\Theta_r} N_r^{1/2} \ ,$$

where N_r is the number of light quanta belonging to the rth characteristic vibration. The total energy of the radiation field before considering its interaction with the atom is simply

$$H_{radiation\ field} = \sum_r N_r h\nu_r \ . \tag{71}$$

In the development of the ϕ_i in the orthogonal system the individual terms still depend on the position of the atom in the inclosure. Since the dependence averages out in the final result when the inclosure is sufficiently large, it is convenient to introduce a mean-square amplitude obtained by averaging the square of the true amplitude over all possible positions of the atom. This yields the following expression for ϕ_i:

$$\phi_i=\left(\frac{h}{2\pi c}\right)^{1/2}\sum_r \cos \alpha_{ir}\left(\frac{\nu_r}{\sigma_r}\right)^{1/2}\left[N_r^{1/2}e^{\frac{2\pi i}{h}\Theta_r}+e^{-\frac{2\pi i}{h}\Theta_r}N_r^{1/2}\right] . \quad (72)$$

Here α_{ir} is the angle between the electric vector of the rth characteristic vibration and the q_i-axis, and σ_r is the number of characteristic vibrations in the frequency interval $\Delta\nu_r$ and solid angle $\Delta\omega_r$ divided by $\Delta\nu_r\Delta\omega_r$. Thus the Hamiltonian function for the complete system is

$$\left.\begin{aligned} H=H_{atom}+\sum_r N_r h\nu_r \\ +\frac{e}{c}\left(\frac{h}{2\pi c}\right)^{1/2}\sum_r \dot{q}_r\left(\frac{\nu_r}{\sigma_r}\right)^{1/2}\left[N_r^{1/2}e^{\frac{2\pi i}{h}\Theta_r}+e^{-\frac{2\pi i}{h}\Theta_r}N_r^{1/2}\right] , \end{aligned}\right\} (73)$$

where $\dot{q}_r$ is the component of the vector $\dot{\boldsymbol{q}}$ in the direction of the electric vector of the rth characteristic vibration.

From equation (73) all the results obtained above by the use of the conservation laws may immediately be deduced. Thus the constancy of H may be proved as in the Appendix (§ 1, p. 121), and it further follows that for the emission or absorption of a light quantum $h\nu_r$ the essential factor is the matrix element of $\dot{q}_r$ corresponding to the transition concerned. Except for certain numerical factors which will not be calculated here the transition probability is given directly by the square of this matrix element. If the calculation is carried out (the interaction terms being regarded as perturbations), emission and absorption processes appear as first-order effects and dispersion phenomena as second order. For the details of the calculation the reader is referred to the papers of Dirac.[1]

The formulation of the Hamiltonian of the radiation problem in equation (73) has the disadvantage that it does not appear to involve the interference and coherence properties of the radiation. This is only the case, however, when mean amplitudes are used, as in the foregoing. If the correct amplitudes resulting from the development of the Φ_i in the orthogonal functions are retained, then the fact that these functions are solutions of the Maxwell equations assures interference and coherence properties for the radiation that correspond to the Maxwell equations. For example, solutions of the Maxwell equations appear as factors of the quantities a_r in A (113) and these factors disappear at the position occupied by the atom when the vector potential vanishes there because of interference. Thus there will be no absorption of light in regions where there would be none according to the classical interference theory. From these considerations it follows at once that the classical wave theory is sufficient for the discussion of all questions of coherence and interference.

§ 5. INTERFERENCE AND THE CONSERVATION LAWS

It is very difficult for us to conceive the fact that the theory of photons does not conflict with the requirements of the Maxwell equations. There have been attempts to avoid the contradiction by finding solutions of the latter which represent "needle" radiation (unidirectional

[1] Dirac (*loc. cit.*) uses the original Schrödinger form in place of the Hamiltonian function (73). With the use of (73) the calculation is somewhat simpler, since the quadratic terms in ϕi drop out of the interaction energy. The results are the same as those of Dirac.

beams), but the results could not be satisfactorily interpreted until the principles of the quantum theory had been elucidated. These show us that whenever an experiment is capable of furnishing information regarding the direction of emission of a photon, its results are precisely those which would be predicted from a solution of the Maxwell equations of the needle type (cf. the reduction of wave-packets, II, § 2c).

As an example, the recoil produced by the emission of a photon will be discussed. Let an atom go from stationary state n to m with the emission of a photon, and an appropriate change of its total momentum. As we are only concerned with the coherence properties of the emitted radiation, we use the correspondence-principle method, in which the radiation is calculated classically. As source of the radiation we take a charge distribution which is modeled after the expression which would be given by the classical theory of matter waves. The atom will be supposed to consist of one electron (of mass μ, charge $-e$, co-ordinates $\boldsymbol{r}_e$) and a nucleus (of mass M, charge $+e$, co-ordinates $\boldsymbol{r}_n$). The Schrödinger function of the nth state, in which the atom has the total momentum $\boldsymbol{P}$, is

$$e^{\frac{2\pi i}{h}\boldsymbol{P}\cdot\boldsymbol{r}_c}\psi_n(\boldsymbol{r}_e-\boldsymbol{r}_n)e^{\frac{2\pi i}{h}Et},$$

where $\boldsymbol{r}_c=(\mu\boldsymbol{r}_e+M\boldsymbol{r}_n)/(\mu+M)$ is the vector to the center of gravity of the atom. If the matrix element of the probability density associated to the transition $n\rightarrow m$, $\boldsymbol{P}\rightarrow\boldsymbol{P}'$, $E\rightarrow E'$, be calculated, one obtains

$$e^{\frac{2\pi i}{h}(\boldsymbol{P}-\boldsymbol{P}')\cdot\boldsymbol{r}_c}\psi_n(\boldsymbol{r}_e-\boldsymbol{r}_n)\psi_m^*(\boldsymbol{r}_e-\boldsymbol{r}_n)e^{-\frac{2\pi i}{h}(E-E')t}.$$

By averaging over the co-ordinates of the nucleus, one obtains the charge density due to the electron, by averaging over the co-ordinates of the electron, that due to the nucleus; the total charge density is their sum. This density is to be considered as the virtual source of the emitted radiation, at least in so far as its coherence properties are concerned. The two component densities are [the common factor e is omitted, $\boldsymbol{r}=\boldsymbol{r}_e-\boldsymbol{r}_n$ is the variable of integration, dv the volume element, and $\gamma=M/(\mu+M)$]

$$\rho_e=e^{\frac{2\pi i}{h}(\boldsymbol{P}-\boldsymbol{P}')\cdot\boldsymbol{r}_e}\int e^{\frac{2\pi i}{h}\gamma(\boldsymbol{P}-\boldsymbol{P}')\cdot\boldsymbol{r}}\psi_n\psi_m^* dv\cdot e^{\frac{2\pi i}{h}(E-E')t},$$

$$\rho_n=e^{\frac{2\pi i}{h}(\boldsymbol{P}-\boldsymbol{P}')\cdot\boldsymbol{r}_n}\int e^{\frac{2\pi i}{h}\gamma(P-P')\cdot\boldsymbol{r}}\psi_n\psi_m^* dv\cdot e^{\frac{2\pi i}{h}(E-E')t}.$$

The total density is thus

$$\rho=\text{Const.}\ e^{\frac{2\pi i}{h}[(\boldsymbol{P}-\boldsymbol{P}')\cdot\boldsymbol{r}-(E-E')t]},$$

in which the value of the constant does not interest us. The current densities are given by analogous expressions. The radiation emitted by these charges is to be calculated from the retarded potentials:

$$\Phi_0=\int\rho(t-R'/c)/R'\cdot dv$$

is the scalar potential and analogous expressions may be obtained for the vector potentials Φ_i (R' is the distance from the point of integration, $\boldsymbol{r}$, to the point of observation $\boldsymbol{R}$). The result is therefore

$$\Phi_0=\text{Const.}\int\frac{\exp\frac{2\pi i}{h}[(\boldsymbol{P}-\boldsymbol{P}')\cdot\boldsymbol{r}-(E-E')(t-R'/c)]}{R'}dv.$$

If one supposes that an experiment has determined the position of the atom with a given accuracy (the value of the momentum $\boldsymbol{P}$ must then be correspondingly uncertain), then this means that the density ρ is given by the foregoing expression only in a finite volume Δv, and is zero elsewhere. If the radiation at a great distance from Δv is required, R' may be expanded in terms of $\boldsymbol{R}$ (the co-ordinates of the point of observation) and $\boldsymbol{r}$ (the co-ordinates of the point of integration):

$$R' = R - \boldsymbol{R}_1 \cdot \boldsymbol{r} ,$$

where $\boldsymbol{R}_1 = \boldsymbol{R}/R$. The scalar potential is then given by

$$\Phi_0 = \text{Const. } e^{\frac{2\pi i}{h}(t - R/c)} \int (1/R) e^{\frac{2\pi i}{h}(\boldsymbol{P} - \boldsymbol{P}' - h\nu \boldsymbol{R}_1/c) \cdot \boldsymbol{r}} dv ,$$

in which $h\nu = E - E'$.

The integral is appreciably different from zero only in that regions for which the factor of $\boldsymbol{r}$ in the exponential is less in absolute magnitude than the reciprocal of Δl, the linear dimension of Δv. In all other regions, the radiation from different portions of Δv is destroyed by interference. Hence

$$\boldsymbol{P} - \boldsymbol{P}' = h\nu \boldsymbol{R}_1/c \pm h/\Delta l ,$$

and the atom recoils with the momentum $h\nu \boldsymbol{R}_1/c$ (except for the natural uncertainty $h/\Delta l$). If the direction of recoil is determined by some experimental procedure, the emitted radiation thus behaves like a unidirectional beam. This is only a special case, however, which is realized only when $\boldsymbol{P}$ and $\boldsymbol{P}'$ are determined with sufficient accuracy, and the co-ordinates of the center of gravity are correspondingly unknown. The other extreme is realized when the experiment fixes the position of the atom more precisely than $\Delta l = h/|\boldsymbol{P} - \boldsymbol{P}'| = c/\nu$, i.e., more precisely than one wave-length of the emitted radiation. The expression for Φ_0 then represents a regular spherical wave and no conclusions can be drawn concerning the recoil, since its uncertainty is greater than its probable value.

This example illustrates very clearly how the quantum theory strips even the light waves of the primitive reality which is ascribed to them by the classical theory. The particular solution of the Maxwell equation which represents the emitted radiation depends on the accuracy with which the co-ordinates of the center of mass of the atom are known.

§ 6. THE COMPTON EFFECT AND THE EXPERIMENT OF COMPTON AND SIMON

There are analogous relations in the theory of the Compton effect, but even though the calculations are the same as those of the preceding paragraph, a summary of the essential results will be given here. It is more interesting to consider bound electrons than free electrons, for then (if one assumes the position of the stationary atomic nucleus as given) there is a certain a priori knowledge concerning the position of the scattering electron. The laws of conservation result in the equations

$$\left.\begin{aligned} h\nu + E &= h\nu' + E' \,, \\ \frac{h\nu}{c}\,\boldsymbol{e} \pm \sim\Delta \boldsymbol{p} &= \frac{h\nu'}{c}\,\boldsymbol{e}' + \boldsymbol{p}' \,, \end{aligned}\right\} \tag{74}$$

The unprimed letters refer to variables before the collision, and the primed ones to variables after the collision;

$\boldsymbol{p}$ is the linear momentum of the electron, and $\boldsymbol{e}$ and $\boldsymbol{e}'$ signify unit vectors in the direction of motion of the light quantum; $\Delta\boldsymbol{p}$ gives the range of momentum of the electron in the atom. If $\sim\Delta\boldsymbol{p}$ is small compared with $\boldsymbol{p}$ and $h\nu/c$, then (74) enables correspondingly exact conclusions regarding the relation between the directions $\boldsymbol{e}'$ and $\boldsymbol{p}'$ to be drawn. If, for example, $\boldsymbol{p}'$ be measured in a Wilson chamber, then the radiation will have all the properties of needle radiation, since the direction of emission of the light quantum is determined. If $\boldsymbol{p}' \gg \Delta\boldsymbol{p}$, then the translational wave function may be regarded as that of a plane wave, namely, $exp\ 2\pi i/h \cdot (\boldsymbol{p}' \cdot \boldsymbol{r} - E't)$, where $\boldsymbol{r}$ is the vector specifying the position of the electron. Let the wave function of the unperturbed state E, which will be assumed to be the normal state, be $\psi_E(\boldsymbol{r})\ exp\ 2\pi i/h \cdot Et$, where ψ_E is different from zero in an interval $\Delta l [\Delta l \cdot \Delta p \sim h]$.

These wave functions are perturbed by the incident wave of frequency ν, and the perturbation function is a periodic space function of wave-length $\lambda = c/\nu$. Therefore, as the final result for the perturbed charge distribution, one obtains an expression of the form

$$\left.\begin{aligned} \rho &= c f_E(\boldsymbol{r}) e^{-\frac{2\pi i}{h} Et}\, e^{\frac{2\pi i}{h}\left(\frac{\boldsymbol{r}\cdot\boldsymbol{e}}{\lambda} - \nu t\right)}\, e^{-\frac{2\pi i}{h}(\boldsymbol{p}\cdot\boldsymbol{r} - E't)} \\ &= c f_E(\boldsymbol{r}) e^{\frac{2\pi i}{h}\left[\left(\frac{h\nu}{c}\boldsymbol{e} - \boldsymbol{p}'\right)\cdot\boldsymbol{r} - (E - E' + h\nu)t\right]}, \end{aligned}\right\} \quad (75)$$

Where f_E is different from zero only in the interval Δl. If one writes the retarded potentials for points at a great distance from the atom, then[1]

$$\Phi_0(R) = c\, e^{-2\pi i \nu'\left(t - \frac{R}{c}\right)} \int_{\text{atom}} \frac{dv'}{R'} f_E(\boldsymbol{r}') e^{\frac{2\pi i}{h}\left(\frac{h\nu}{c}\boldsymbol{e} - \boldsymbol{p}' - \frac{h\nu'}{c}\boldsymbol{e}'\right)\cdot\boldsymbol{r}'} . \quad (76)$$

[1] G. Breit, *Journal of the Optical Society of America*, 14, 324, 1927.

In this equation $h\nu' = E - E' + h\nu$, $\boldsymbol{r}'$ is the vector to the point of integration, $\boldsymbol{R}$ to the point of observation, and $\boldsymbol{R}' = \boldsymbol{R} - \boldsymbol{r}'$. The time factor in equation (76) shows that the frequency of the scattered radiation is ν' and corresponds to that of equation (74). Furthermore, the integral on the right-hand side of equation (76) vanishes because of interference, if the factor of $\boldsymbol{r}'$ is materially greater than the reciprocal atomic diameter. Accordingly, since $\Delta l \Delta p \sim h$,

$$\frac{h\nu}{c}\,\boldsymbol{e} = \frac{h\nu'}{c}\,\boldsymbol{e}' + \boldsymbol{p}' \pm \sim \Delta \boldsymbol{p}\,, \tag{77}$$

in agreement with the second equation of (74). The scattered radiation behaves, therefore, in so far as its coherence properties are concerned, like needle radiation. However, the direction of the light quantum is not exactly prescribed, which may be regarded as a consequence of the indeterminateness of the momentum in the original stationary state. This indeterminateness can be diminished if one experiments with more loosely bound electrons, but then the atomic cross-section will be correspondingly greater. If one applies the considerations to an excited state, then $\Delta l \Delta p \sim nh$ appears in place of $\Delta l \Delta p \sim h$ and in the evaluation of the retarded potentials one must take the number of nodes of $\psi(\boldsymbol{r}')$ into account. Since this involves only nonessential complications, we have confined ourselves to the normal state.

If one wishes to explain the Geiger-Bothe experiment on the simultaneity of emission of recoil electron and scattered photon, then if the correspondence principle methods sketched here are used, one must deal with charge distributions which radiate only during a definite time interval. The initial state of the electron will be given, by a wave-packet at rest, whose size depends on the experimental arrangement. The final state will be represented by a morning wave-packet, and the charge density, given by the product of the two wave functions, will then be different from zero only during the time the two packets overlap. The radiation produced will then be a finite wave train moving in a definite direction. A more consequent explanation of the Geiger-Bothe experiment, even though it is equivalent in all its essential points, can only be obtained from the quantum theory of radiation. Moreover, as already shown, in this theory the laws of conservation applied to light quanta and electrons hold, so that one can, without any misgivings, use the customary corpuscular theory of this experiment.

§ 7. RADIATION FLUCTUATION PHENOMENA

The large mean-square fluctuations, which belong to a corpuscular theory, are contained in the mathematical framework of the quantum theory, as shown in the Appendix. It is especially instructive, however, to study the relations between the various physical pictures with which the quantum theory operates by calculating the fluctuation of a radiation field. Let there be given a black cavity, of volume V, containing radiation in temperature equilibrium. The mean energy $\overline{\mathfrak{E}}$ contained in a small volume element ΔV in the frequency range between ν and $\nu+\Delta\nu$ is, according to Planck's formula,

$$\overline{\mathfrak{E}}=\frac{8\pi^2 h\nu}{c^3}\frac{\Delta\nu\Delta V}{e^{h\nu/kT}-1}\;; \tag{78}$$

k is the Boltzmann constant and T the temperature. According to general thermodynamic laws,[1] the following relation holds for the mean-square fluctuation of $\mathfrak{E}$:

$$\overline{\Delta \mathfrak{E}^2} = kT^2 \frac{d\overline{\mathfrak{E}}}{dT} .$$

Substituting into equation (78), it was shown by Einstein that

$$\overline{\Delta \mathfrak{E}^2} = \underbrace{h\nu \overline{\mathfrak{E}}}_{\text{corpuscle}} + \underbrace{\frac{c^3}{8\pi^2\nu^2 \Delta\nu \Delta V}}_{\text{wave}} \overline{\mathfrak{E}}^2 . \tag{79}$$

This value for the mean-square fluctuation can only be derived partially with the help of the classical theory. The corpuscular viewpoint yields

$$\overline{\mathfrak{E}} = h\nu\bar{n} . \tag{80}$$

The classical particle theory thus results only in the first part of formula (79). The classical wave theory of radiation, on the other hand, leads exactly to the second part of (79). The calculations for this will be given later in connection with the quantum theory. Thus, the quantum theory proper is necessary for the derivation of formula (79), in which it is naturally immaterial whether one uses the wave or the corpuscular picture.

If, in particular, one treats the problem by means of the configuration space of the particles (although it is true that this has not been done in a detailed manner for

[1] J. W. Gibbs, *Elementary Principles in Statistical Mechanics*, pp. 70–72, 1902.

light quanta), then one must note that the whole term system of the problem can be subdivided into non-combining partial systems, from which a definite one can be chosen as a solution. Because of the exchange relations (84), which become apparent from the corresponding uncertainty relations, that term system must be taken whose characteristic functions are symmetric in the co-ordinates of the light quanta. This choice leads to the Bose statistics for the light quanta and also, as Bose[1] has shown, to equation (78).

If the wave picture be used, then one obtains the number of light quanta corresponding to the vibration concerned from the amplitudes of the characteristic vibrations, and therefore the same mathematical scheme. In order to avoid unnecessary complications in the calculations, let us treat a vibrating string of length l instead of the black radiation cavity. Let $\varphi(x, t)$ be its lateral displacement, and c the velocity of sound in the string. The Lagrangian function becomes

$$L=\frac{1}{2}\left[\frac{1}{c^2}\left(\frac{\partial\varphi}{\partial t}\right)^2-\left(\frac{\partial\varphi}{\partial x}\right)^2\right], \tag{81}$$

whence (A § 9)

$$\Pi=\frac{1}{c^2}\frac{\partial\varphi}{\partial t}, \tag{82}$$

and

$$\overline{H}=\frac{1}{2}\int_0^l\left\{c^2\Pi^2+\left(\frac{\partial\varphi}{\partial x}\right)^2\right\}=\frac{1}{2}\int_0^l\left\{\frac{1}{c^2}\left(\frac{\partial\varphi}{\partial t}\right)^2+\left(\frac{\partial\varphi}{\partial x}\right)^2\right\}dx. \tag{83}$$

The following exchange relations are to be used:

$$\Pi(x)\varphi(x')-\varphi(x')\Pi(x)=\delta(x-x')\frac{h}{2\pi i}. \tag{84}$$

[1] *Zeitschrift für Physik*, **26**, 178, 1924.

With the introduction of

$$\varphi(x,t)=\sqrt{\frac{2}{l}}\sum_k q_k(t)\sin\frac{k\pi x}{l}\,,$$

$\overline{H}$ goes over into

$$\overline{H}=\tfrac{1}{2}\sum_k\left\{\frac{1}{c^2}\dot{q}_k^2+\left(\frac{k\pi}{l}\right)^2 q_k^2\right\}. \tag{85}$$

On introducing the momenta associated to q_k,

$$p_k=\frac{1}{c^2}\dot{q}_k\,, \tag{86}$$

equation (84) becomes

$$p_k q_l - q_l p_k = \delta_{kl}\,\frac{h}{2\pi i} \tag{87}$$

or

$$\left.\begin{aligned} p_k&=\sqrt{\frac{k\pi}{l}}\sqrt{\frac{h}{2\pi}}\left\{N_k^{\frac{1}{2}}e^{\frac{2\pi i}{h}\Theta_k}+e^{-\frac{2\pi i}{h}\Theta_k}N_k^{\frac{1}{2}}\right\}\\ q_k&=\sqrt{\frac{k\pi}{l}}\sqrt{\frac{h}{2\pi}}\left\{N_k^{\frac{1}{2}}e^{\frac{2\pi i}{h}\Theta_k}-e^{-\frac{2\pi i}{h}\Theta_k}N_k^{\frac{1}{2}}\right\}\frac{1}{i}\,. \end{aligned}\right\} \tag{88}$$

The characteristic frequencies of the string are $\nu_k = k(c/2l)$, and therefore

$$\overline{H}=\sum_k h\nu_k(N_k+\tfrac{1}{2})\,. \tag{89}$$

For the energy in a small section (0, a) of the string, one obtains, however,

$$\mathbf{E}=\frac{1}{l}\int_0^a\sum_{j,k}\left\{\frac{1}{c^2}\dot{q}_j\dot{q}_k\sin\frac{j\pi x}{l}\sin\frac{k\pi x}{l}\right.$$
$$\left.+q_j q_k jk\left(\frac{\pi}{l}\right)^2\cos\frac{j\pi x}{l}\cos\frac{k\pi x}{l}\right\}dx\,. \tag{90}$$

If the terms of this sum with $j=k$ be singled out, then under the explicit hypothesis that the wave-lengths to be considered are all small with respect to a, one obtains the value

$$\overline{\mathbb{E}}=\frac{a}{l}\overline{H}\,.$$

One thus finds the fluctuation $\Delta\mathbb{E}=\mathbb{E}-\overline{\mathbb{E}}$ by neglecting the terms with $j=k$ in (90). The integration results in

$$\Delta\mathbb{E}=\frac{1}{2l}\sum_{j\neq k}\left\{\frac{1}{c^2}\,\dot{q}_j\dot{q}_kK_{jk}+jk\left(\frac{\pi}{l}\right)^2 q_jq_kK'_{jk}\right\}, \qquad (91)$$

where

$$\left.\begin{aligned} K_{jk}&=c\,\frac{\sin\,(\nu_j-\nu_k)a/c}{\nu_j-\nu_k}-c\,\frac{\sin\,(\nu_j+\nu_k)a/c}{\nu_j+\nu_k}\,,\\ K'_{jk}&=c\,\frac{\sin\,(\nu_j-\nu_k)a/c}{\nu_j-\nu_k}+c\,\frac{\sin\,(\nu_j+\nu_k)a/c}{\nu_j+\nu_k}\,.\end{aligned}\right\} \qquad (92)$$

Accordingly, the mean-square fluctuation is given by

$$\overline{\Delta\mathbb{E}^2}=\frac{1}{2l^2}\sum_{j\neq k}\left\{\frac{1}{c^4}\overline{\dot{q}_j^2}\,\overline{\dot{q}_k^2}\,K_{jk}^2+j^2k^2\left(\frac{\pi}{l}\right)^4\overline{q_j^2}\,\overline{q_k^2}\,K'^2_{jk}\right.$$
$$\left.+\left(\frac{\pi}{l}\right)^2\frac{jk}{c^2}\left(\overline{q_j\dot{q}_j}\,\overline{q_k\dot{q}_k}+\overline{\dot{q}_jq_j}\,\overline{\dot{q}_kq_k}\right)K_{jk}K'_{jk}\right\}.$$

The sums over j and k may be replaced by an integral over the frequencies ν_j and ν_k, respectively, if it be assumed that the string l is very long, so that its characteristic frequencies are close together. In addition, one finally assumes that a is large and uses the relation

$$\lim_{a\to\infty}\frac{1}{a}\int_{-\nu_1}^{\nu_2}\frac{\sin^2\nu a}{\nu^2}f(\nu)d\nu=\pi f(0) \qquad (93)$$

if $\nu_1>0$, $\nu_2>0$. The double integral then becomes a simple integral and one finds that

$$\overline{\Delta\mathfrak{E}^2}=\frac{a}{c}\int d\nu\left\{\frac{1}{c^4}(\overline{\dot{q}_\nu^2})^2+\left[\left(\frac{2\pi\nu}{c}\right)^2\overline{q_\nu^2}\right]^2+\frac{1}{c^2}\left(\frac{2\pi\nu}{c}\right)^2[(\overline{q_\nu\dot{q}_\nu})^2+(\overline{\dot{q}_\nu q_\nu})^2]\right\}. \quad (94)$$

Because of the exchange relations (84),

$$\overline{q_\nu\dot{q}_\nu}=-\overline{\dot{q}_\nu q_\nu}=c^2\frac{h}{4\pi i}, \quad (95)$$

so that

$$\overline{\mathfrak{E}}=\frac{a}{l}\int d\nu\, Z_\nu\, h\nu(N_\nu+\tfrac{1}{2}), \quad (96)$$

where $Z_\nu d\nu$ denotes the number of characteristic frequencies in the interval $d\nu$, or, in this case, $Z_\nu=2l/c$. If the integral be taken over the frequency interval $\Delta\nu$, one obtains

$$\overline{\mathfrak{E}}=\frac{a}{l}Z_\nu\,\Delta\nu\, h\nu(N_\nu+\tfrac{1}{2}), \quad (97)$$

$$\overline{\Delta\mathfrak{E}^2}=\frac{a}{c}\Delta\nu\left[\tfrac{1}{2}\left(\frac{\overline{\mathfrak{E}}c}{a\Delta\nu}\right)^2-\tfrac{1}{2}(h\nu)^2\right]. \quad (98)$$

One then subdivides $\overline{\mathfrak{E}}$ into the thermal energy $\overline{\mathfrak{E}^*}$ and the zero point energy:

$$\overline{\mathfrak{E}}=\overline{\mathfrak{E}^*}+\frac{a}{l}Z_\nu\,\Delta\nu\frac{h\nu}{2}=\overline{\mathfrak{E}^*}+a\,\Delta\nu\, h\nu,$$

and finds

$$\overline{\Delta\mathfrak{E}^2}=\frac{a}{2c}\Delta\nu\left[\left(\frac{\overline{\mathfrak{E}^*}c}{a\Delta\nu}\right)^2+2\frac{\overline{\mathfrak{E}^*}c}{a\Delta\nu}h\nu\right]$$

$$=h\nu\overline{\mathfrak{E}^*}+\frac{\overline{\mathfrak{E}^*}^2}{\Delta\nu}Z_\nu\frac{a}{l}. \quad (99)$$

This value corresponds exactly to formula (79). The corresponding relation in the classical wave theory may be obtained by passing to the limit $h=0$ in (99). The classical wave theory thus leads only to the second term of equation (99). The quantum theory, which one can interpret as a particle theory or as a wave theory as one sees fit, leads to the complete fluctuation formula.

§ 8. RELATIVISTIC FORMULATION OF THE QUANTUM THEORY

The conditions imposed on all physical theories by the principle of relativity have been neglected in most of the foregoing discussions, and consequently the results obtained are applicable only under those conditions in which the velocity of light may be regarded as infinite. The reason for this neglect is that all relativistic effects belong to the *terra incognita* of quantum theory; the physical principles which have been elucidated in this book must be valid in this region also and thus it seemed proper not to obscure them with questions that cannot be aswered definitely at the present time. None the less, this book would be incomplete without a brief discussion of the attempts to construct theories which shall embody both sets of principles, and the difficulties which have arisen in these attempts.

Dirac[1] has set up a wave equation which is valid for one electron and is invariant under the Lorentz transformation. It fulfils all requirements of the quantum theory, and is able to give a good account of the phenomena of the "spinning" electron, which could previously only be

[1] P. A. M. Dirac, *Proceedings of the Royal Society*, A, **117**, 610, 1928.

treated by *ad hoc* assumptions. The essential difficulty which arises with all relativistic quantum theories is not eliminated however. This arises from the relation

$$\frac{1}{c^2}E^2=\mu^2c^2+p_x^2+p_y^2+p_z^2 \tag{100}$$

between the energy and momentum of a free electron. According to this equation there are two values of E which differ in sign associated with each set of values of p_x, p_y, p_z. The classical theory could eliminate this by arbitrarily excluding the one sign, but this is not possible according to the principles of quantum theory. Here spontaneous transitions may occur to the states of negative energy; as these have never been observed, the theory is certainly wrong. Under these conditions it is very remarkable that the positive energy-levels (at least in the case of one electron) coincide with those actually observed.

The difficulty inherent in formula (100) is also shown by a calculation of O. Klein,[1] who proves that if the electron is governed by any equation based on this relation it will be able to pass unhindered through regions in which its potential energy is greater than $2mc^2$. If only motion in the x-direction be considered the formulas (31*a*) (31*c*) become

$$\frac{E^2}{c^2}=\mu^2c^2+p_x^2\ ,$$

$$\frac{(E-V)^2}{c^2}=\mu^2c^2+p_x'^2\ ,$$

[1] *Zeitschrift für Physik*, **53**, 157, 1929.

whence

$$p_x'^2 = p_x^2 + \frac{(E-v)^2 - E^2}{c^2} ,$$

while the wave function has the form

$$e^{\frac{2\pi i}{h}(p_x' x - Et)} .$$

For very small values of V, p_x' is real and there are transmitted waves, just as in chapter ii, §2*f*. For larger values, p_x' becomes a pure imaginary, so that the wave is totally reflected at the discontinuity and decreases exponentially in region II. But for very large values of V, p_x' again becomes real, i.e., the electron wave again penetrates into the region II with constant amplitude. A more exact calculation verifies this result.

A difficulty of a somewhat different character arises in the calculation of the energy of the field of the electron according to the relativistic theory. For a point electron (one of zero radius) even the classical theory yields an infinite value of the energy, as is well known, so that it becomes necessary to introduce a universal constant of the dimension of a length—the "radius of the electron." It is remarkable that in the non-relativistic theory this difficulty can be avoided in another way—by a suitable choice of the order of non-commutative factors in the Hamiltonian function. This has hitherto not been possible in the relativistic quantum theory.

The hope is often expressed that after these problems have been solved the quantum theory will be seen to be based, in a large measure at least, on classical concepts. But even a superficial survey of the trend of the evolution of physics in the past thirty years shows that it is far more likely that the solution will result in further limitations on the applicability of classical concepts than that it will result in a removal of those already discovered. The list of modifications and limitations of our ideal world—which now contains those required by the relativity theory (for which c is characteristic) and the uncertainty relations (symbolized by Planck's constant h)—will be extended by others which correspond to e, μ, M. But the character of these is as yet not to be anticipated.

APPENDIX[1]

THE MATHEMATICAL APPARATUS OF THE QUANTUM THEORY[2]

For the derivation of the mathematical scheme of the quantum theory, whether based on the wave or the particle picture, two sources are available: empirical facts and the correspondence principle. The correspondence principle, which is due to Bohr,[3] postulates a detailed analogy between the quantum theory and the classical theory appropriate to the mental picture employed. This analogy does not merely serve as a guide to the discovery of formal laws; its special value is that it furnishes the interpretation of the laws that are found in terms of the mental picture used.

We commence with a derivation of the mathematical structure of quantum mechanics from the corpuscular analogy.[4]

§ 1. THE CORPUSCULAR CONCEPT OF MATTER

The fundamental equations of classical mechanics for a system of f-degrees of freedom may be written in the so-called "canonical" form,

$$\dot{p}_k = -\frac{\partial H}{\partial q_k}, \quad \dot{q}_k = \frac{\partial H}{\partial p_k}, \qquad (k = 1, 2, \ldots, f), \qquad (1)$$

[1] Unless otherwise indicated equation numbers and section numbers refer to the Appendix.

[2] Cf. Translators' note in Preface.

[3] Cf. N. Bohr, *Zeitschrift für Physik*, **13**, 117, 1923.

[4] W. Heisenberg, *ibid.*, **33**, 879, 1925; M. Born and P. Jordan, *ibid.*, **34**, 858, 1925; M. Born, W. Heisenberg, and P. Jordan, *ibid.*, **35**, 557, 1926. Cf. also W. Heisenberg, *Mathematische Annalen*, **95**, 683, 1926.

where $q_1, q_2, \ldots, q_f$ are the generalized co-ordinates, $p_1, p_2, \ldots, p_f$ their conjugate momenta, and H the Hamiltonian function. When H does not depend explicitly on the time the energy equation

$$H(p, q) = W\ , \qquad (2)$$

where W, the total energy, is a constant, follows at once. For simplicity it may be assumed that the system is multiply periodic, in which case any co-ordinate q_k as a function of the time may be written as a Fourier series, that is, as a sum of harmonic terms in the form

$$q_k = \sum_{\tau_1=-\infty}^{+\infty} \sum_{\tau_2=-\infty}^{+\infty} \cdots \sum_{\tau_f=-\infty}^{+\infty} q^{(k)}_{\tau_1, \tau_2, \ldots, \tau_f}\ e^{2\pi i(\tau_1\nu_1+\tau_2\nu_2+\ldots\tau_f\nu_f)t}\ . \qquad (3)$$

The $q^{(k)}_{\tau_1, \tau_2, \ldots, \tau_f}$ are amplitudes independent of the time and $\nu_1, \nu_2, \ldots, \nu_f$ are the fundamental frequencies of the motion. Similar expressions involving the same frequencies may be written for the p_k and in general for any function of the p_k and q_k.

By a canonical transformation—that is, one which leaves invariant the form of equations (1)—it is possible to introduce a new set of canonical conjugates J_k, w_k, known as "action-angle variables." These are essentially defined by the following properties: The Hamiltonian H depends on the J_k only and the w_k are related to the fundamental frequencies of the motion by equations of the form

$$w_k = \nu_k t + \beta_k$$

where the β_k are constants. In these variables the equations of motion therefore become

$$\dot{J}_k = -\frac{\partial H}{\partial w_k}, \quad \dot{w}_k = \nu_k = \frac{\partial H}{\partial J_k}, \qquad (k=1, 2, \ldots, f) . \tag{4}$$

According to classical electrodynamics the frequencies of the spectral lines emitted by an atom will be the frequencies of the harmonic terms in equation (3) and the amplitudes will determine the corresponding intensities.

According to the correspondence principle there must exist a close relationship between the mechanics of classical particles as outlined above and the mechanics of the quantum theory. For the latter we must therefore seek a set of equations analogous in form to the equations of classical theory, but which also take account of certain well-established empirical facts of atomic physics. Primary among these are the following:

1. *The Rydberg-Ritz combination principle.*—The observed spectral frequencies of an atom possess a characteristic term structure. That is, all the spectral lines of an element may be represented as the differences of a relatively small number of terms. If these terms are arranged in a one-dimensional array $T_1, T_2, \ldots,$ the atomic frequencies form a two-dimensional array

$$\nu(nm) = T_n - T_m , \tag{5}$$

from which follows at once the combination principle

$$\nu(nk) + \nu(km) = \nu(nm) . \tag{6}$$

2. *The existence of discrete energy values.*—The fundamental experiments of Franck and Hertz on electronic impacts show that the energy of an atom can take on only certain definite discrete[1] values, $W_1, W_2, \ldots$ . .

3. *The Bohr frequency relation.*—The characteristic frequencies of an atom are related to its characteristic energies by the equation

$$\nu(nm) = \frac{1}{h}(W_n - W_m) . \qquad (7)$$

We shall now sketch the deduction of the fundamental equations of the new quantum mechanics, following the program outlined above. It should be distinctly understood, however, that this cannot be a deduction in the mathematical sense of the word, since the equations to be obtained form themselves the postulates of the theory. Although made highly plausible by the following considerations, their ultimate justification lies in the agreement of their predictions with experiment.

A profound modification, not only of classical dynamics, but of classical kinematics, is evidently necessary if the simple experimental facts mentioned above are to be incorporated in the foundations of a new theory. In the classical theory all possible motions of the coordinates may be built up by addition from Fourier terms of the kind contained in equation (3), and these may be termed the "kinematic elements," since the quantities with which the theory deals, and in particular the energy,

[1] In general, the atomic energy can also take on continuous values in a certain range. For the time being this "continuous spectrum" may be disregarded, corresponding to the assumption that the system is multiply periodic.

can be expressed in terms of them. Their amplitudes and frequencies are functions of continuously variable constants of integration as well as of the integers $\tau_1 \ldots . \tau_f$, which determine the order of the harmonics. This is in direct contradiction to the existence of only discrete values of the atomic energies and frequencies and, in fact, to the very existence of sharply defined spectral lines.

Similar elements must be assumed in quantum mechanics if a correspondence is to be preserved between the two theories. To assure the existence of discrete energy values at the outset, the elements will be taken to be functions of integers. Corresponding to the Rydberg-Ritz combination principle, a dependence on two sets of integers is required, while the f-fold character of the classical harmonics suggests that each set contain f integers. We therefore postulate elements of the form

$$q(n_1 \ldots n_f\,;\ m_1 \ldots m_f)e^{2\pi i\nu(n_1 \ldots n_f;\ m_1 \ldots m_f)t}\,, \qquad (8)$$

in which the complexes $n_1 \ldots . n_f$ and $m_1 \ldots . m_f$ replace the single integers n and m in an easily understandable way. Furthermore, the amplitudes and frequencies are assumed to be directly those which are given by a spectral analysis of the emitted radiation, so that the new theory may be described as a calculus of observable quantities. The frequencies $\nu(n_1 \ldots . n_f;\ m_1 \ldots . m_f)$ are therefore assumed to have the term structure (5); they accordingly obey the combination principle (6).

There can clearly be no question of the addition of such elements to form a Fourier series as in the classical theory; there must, however, be an analogue to the representation of a co-ordinate by such a series. A sufficiently general and flexible method is afforded by taking simply the ensemble of all elements of the form (8) as the entity which, in the quantum theory of the particle picture, replaces mathematically the classical representation of a co-ordinate given in equation (3). The ensemble may be written as a matrix,

$$\left\| q(n_1 \ldots n_f\,;\; m_1 \ldots m_f) e^{2\pi i\nu(n_1 \ldots n_f;\, m_1 \ldots m_f)t} \right\| ,$$

that is, as an infinite quadratic array, ordered according to the integers n_i, m_i, which take on all real values. The new kinematics is accordingly based on a matrix representation of the co-ordinates, with

$$q_k = \left\| q_k(nm) e^{2\pi i\nu(nm)t} \right\| \tag{9}$$

corresponding to q_k. As here, the complexes $n_1 \ldots n_f$ and $m_1 \ldots m_f$ will, in general, be replaced by single letters n and m. For the momenta p_k a similar matrix representation is assumed, with the same frequencies, as is the case in classical Fourier series.[1]

Such a representation is, however, meaningless both mathematically and physically until properties and rules of operation for the matrices have been defined. The correspondence principle must be our guide here. In the first place, the classical expression (3) must have a real value; since the terms are complex this can be the case only if for each term there occurs the conjugate imaginary. This

[1] For a system which is not multiply periodic, matrices with continuously variable indices must be used, corresponding to a classical representation by Fourier integrals.

will also be true of the elements of the matrix (9) if we assume

$$q_k(mn) = q_k^*(nm) \; ,$$

since by (6) $\nu(mn) = -\nu(nm)$. The asterisk denotes the conjugate imaginary. Matrices with this type of symmetry are called Hermitian and in the quantum theory all co-ordinate matrices are assumed to be of this kind.

The time derivative $\dot{q}_k$ of any co-ordinate is represented classically by the Fourier series whose terms are the time derivatives of those of the series representing q_k. Hence for the quantum-theory matrices

$$\dot{q} \equiv \left\| \; 2\pi i\nu(nm) q(nm) e^{2\pi i\nu(nm)t} \; \right\| \; , \tag{10}$$

which is again a Hermitian matrix of the form (9).

It must be possible in the quantum theory to answer such elementary kinematical questions as the following. Given the matrices representing, say, a momentum p and a co-ordinate q, what matrices represent $p+q$, pq, and in general any function of p and q? In the case of addition the answer is obvious from the classical analogue. Since the sum of two Fourier series of the form (3) is again a series of the same kind and with the same frequencies, but with amplitudes which are the sums of the component amplitudes, we must expect for the elements of the quantum-theory matrices

$$(p+q)(nm) \equiv \left\| \; [p(nm) + q(nm)] e^{2\pi i\nu(nm)t} \; \right\| \; .$$

The rule for multiplication is defined from similar considerations with, however, a characteristic difference from classical multiplication, due to the fact that the quantum frequencies obey the Rydberg-Ritz combination principle. The product of two Fourier series in the classical theory may be written as the double sum

$$pq = \sum_{\sigma} \sum_{\sigma'} p_{\sigma} q_{\sigma'} e^{2\pi i[(\sigma+\sigma')\nu]t} ,$$

where σ replaces the complex $\sigma_1 \ldots . \sigma_f$ and $[(\sigma+\sigma')\nu]$ stands for $(\sigma_1+\sigma_1')\nu_1+ \ldots . +(\sigma_f+\sigma_f')\nu_f$. To write this again in the form of equation (3) terms of the same frequency must be collected, i.e., those for which $\sigma+\sigma'=\tau$, giving

$$pq = \sum_{\tau} (pq)_{\tau} e^{2\pi i[\tau\nu]t} ,$$

where

$$(pq)_{\tau} = \sum_{\sigma} p_{\sigma} q_{\tau-\sigma} . \tag{11}$$

In the quantum theory the matrix representing pq must be an ensemble made up of terms $p(nm)e^{2\pi i\nu(nm)t}$ and $q(nm)e^{2\pi i\nu(nm)t}$. A matrix of the type (9) is again obtained if all elements with the same frequency are added together, i.e., those for which $\nu(nk)+\nu(km)=\nu(nm)$ by the combination principle (6). The new amplitudes are therefore taken to be

$$pq(nm) = \sum_{k} p(nk)q(km) , \tag{12}$$

and the elements are then $pq(nm)e^{2\pi i\nu(nm)t}$.

This is the well-known mathematical rule for the multiplication of matrices or tensors, and justifies the use of these terms here. As is obvious from equation (12), $pq(nm) \neq qp(nm)$, so that multiplication in the quantum theory is non-commutative—a result of great importance for the further development.

By means of the rules for addition and multiplication a meaning is given to any function $x(p, q)$ of the coordinate and momentum matrices, at least in so far as the function may be expressed as a power series. The elements of the function x will always be of the form $x(nm)e^{2\pi i\nu(nm)t}$ and the array of frequencies $\nu(nm)$ will always be the same for a given atomic system. Hence a matrix is sufficiently well represented by its amplitudes $x(nm)$ alone, the exponential terms being understood.

The customary definitions and conventions of the theory of matrices are adopted in the quantum theory. Equality of two matrices means equality of corresponding elements. The unit matrix is defined as the matrix whose diagonal elements are all unity and whose non-diagonal elements are zero. It is conveniently written

$$1 \equiv \left\| \delta_{nm} \right\| ,$$

where

$$\delta_{nm} = \begin{cases} 1 \text{ when } n = m , \\ 0 \text{ when } n \neq m . \end{cases}$$

The reciprocal x^{-1} of a matrix x is the matrix satisfying the equations

$$x^{-1}x = xx^{-1} = 1 .$$

The transpose $\tilde{x}$ of x is the matrix $||x(mn)||$ obtained by interchanging the rows and columns of x.

We are now in possession of the elements of a quantum algebra, in which it is readily seen that all the rules of ordinary algebra remain valid with the exception of the commutative law. Thus if x, y, and z represent any functions of the dynamical variables they obey, in the quantum theory, the rules of matrix algebra:

$$x+y=y+x\ ,$$

$$x(y+z)=xy+xz\ ,$$

$$x(yz)=(xy)z\ ,$$

$$(x+y)+z=x+(y+z)\ ,$$

but, in general,

$$xy\neq yx\ .$$

So far the Planck constant h, which must play a fundamental rôle, has not been introduced into the theory. Its appearance proves to be closely related to the non-commutativity of the variables which forms so striking a contrast to the classical theory. In fact, it has been found by Dirac[1] that in the quantum theory the expression $(2\pi i/h)(xy-yx)$ is the analogue of the Poisson bracket

$$[xy]=\sum_{k=1}^{f}\left(\frac{\partial x}{\partial q_k}\frac{\partial y}{\partial p_k}-\frac{\partial y}{\partial q_k}\frac{\partial x}{\partial p_k}\right)$$

in classical mechanics. The invariance of this expression with respect to canonical transformations of the p_k and

[1] P. A. M. Dirac, *Proceedings of the Royal Society*, A, **109**, 642, 1925.

q_k is well known. In order to make plausible this significant connection it will be shown that in the limiting region where the integers n and m are large compared to their differences there is asymptotic agreement between the matrix elements of $(2\pi i/h)(xy-yx)$ and the harmonic elements of the classical bracket expression $[xy]$. It is first necessary, however, to state more exactly the connection between the matrix elements and the Fourier amplitudes.

It will be recalled that in the theory of stationary states, which formed a preliminary stage in the development of the present quantum mechanics, the existence of only discrete energy values is attained through the fixation of "stationary" classical motions. If these are defined from among the continuum of possible motions by the equations[1]

$$J_k = n_k h \qquad (k=1, 2, \ldots, f), \tag{13}$$

where the J_k are the action variables and the n_k integers, the Bohr frequency condition (7) then appears as the analogue of the classical relation

$$\nu_k = \frac{\partial H}{\partial J_k}.$$

For since H is a function of the n_k only by equations (4), $\partial H/\partial J_k$ may be written

$$\frac{\partial H}{\partial J_k} = \lim_{a_k \doteq 0} \frac{H(n_1 \ldots n_f) - H(n_1 \ldots n_k - a_k, \ldots, n_f)}{a_k h},$$

[1] A possible degeneracy is here neglected.

and in the limiting region where the n_k are very large compared to the α_k,

$$\nu(n_1 \,.\,.\, n_f;\, m_1 \,.\,.\, m_f) = \frac{1}{h}\,[H(n_1 \,.\,.\, n_f) - H(n_1 - \alpha_1, \,.\,.\,, n_f - \alpha_f)]$$

$$\sim \alpha_1 \frac{\partial H}{\partial n_1} + \,.\,.\, + \alpha_f \frac{\partial H}{\partial n_f}$$

$$= \alpha_1 \nu_1 + \,.\,.\, + \alpha_f \nu_f \,.$$

There is therefore asymptotic agreement in this region, which may be briefly referred to as that of large quantum integers, between the spectral frequency $\nu(n_1 \,.\,.\,.\,.\, n_f;\, m_1 \,.\,.\,.\,.\, m_f)$ and the harmonic $(n_1 - m_1)\nu_1 + \,.\,.\,.\,. + (n_f - m_f)\nu_f$ in the $(n_1 \,.\,.\,.\,.\, n_f)$ or $(m_1 \,.\,.\,.\,.\, m_f)$ stationary state. Since the harmonic elements of the matrices of quantum mechanics represent the spectral lines this suggests a general co-ordination between the matrix element $q(n_1 \,.\,.\,.\,.\, n_f;\, n_1 - \alpha_1, \,.\,.\,.\,., n_f - \alpha_f)e^{2\pi i\nu(n_1 \,.\,.\,.\,.\, n_f;\, n_1 - \alpha_1 \,.\,.\,.\,.\, n_f - \alpha_f)t}$ and the harmonic $(\alpha_1 \,.\,.\,.\,.\, \alpha_f)$ in the $(n_1 \,.\,.\,.\,.\, n_f)$ stationary state. More briefly,

$$q(n, n-\alpha)e^{2\pi i\nu(n,n-\alpha)t} \text{ corresponds to } q_\alpha(n)e^{2\pi i[\alpha\nu]t} \qquad (14)$$

in the region of large quantum numbers. This co-ordination is further justified by the approximate agreement found empirically in this region between the intensities calculated classically from the Fourier amplitudes $q_\alpha(n)$ in the stationary states and the intensity of the spectral line $\nu(n, n-\alpha)$. The indices n and m of the matrix elements thus correspond to the quantum numbers of two stationary states, while the diagonal elements $(n = m)$ correspond to the stationary states themselves.

With the aid of the co-ordination (14) the above-mentioned correspondence with the Poisson brackets is readily shown. The (nm) element of $(2\pi i/h)(xy-yx)$ may be written as a sum over α and β of terms of the form $(2\pi i/h)\{x(n, n-\alpha)y(n-\alpha, n-\alpha-\beta)-y(n, n-\beta)x(n-\beta, n-\alpha-\beta)\}$, where $\alpha+\beta=n-m$. On adding and subtracting $x(n-\beta, n-\alpha-\beta)y(n-\alpha, n-\alpha-\beta)$ this becomes

$$\left(\frac{2\pi i}{h}\right)\{[x(n, n-\alpha)-x(n-\beta, n-\alpha-\beta)]y(n-\alpha, n-\alpha-\beta) \\ -[y(n, n-\beta)-y(n-\alpha, n-\alpha-\beta)]x(n-\beta, n-\alpha-\beta)\} .$$

Now in the region of "large quantum numbers" where $\alpha, \beta \ll n$,

$$x(n, n-\alpha)-x(n-\beta, n-\alpha-\beta) \sim h\beta \frac{\partial x_\alpha(n)}{\partial J} ,$$

and

$$y(n-\alpha, n-\alpha-\beta) \sim \frac{1}{2\pi i\beta}\frac{\partial y_\beta(n-\alpha)}{\partial w} \sim \frac{1}{2\pi i\beta}\frac{\partial y_\beta(n)}{\partial w}$$

since the harmonics of y are of the form $y_\beta(n)e^{2\pi i\beta w}$ by equations (4). Hence the foregoing matrix element is approximately[1]

$$\sum_{\alpha+\beta=n-m}\sum_{k=1}^{f}\left[\frac{\partial x_\alpha(n)}{\partial J_k}\frac{\partial y_\beta(n)}{\partial w_k}-\frac{\partial y_\beta(n)}{\partial J_k}\frac{\partial x_\alpha(n)}{\partial w_k}\right] ,$$

[1] The summation necessarily extends into the region where the quantum numbers are not large compared to their difference; hence for numerical agreement the matrix elements far removed from the diagonal must be assumed negligible, since they correspond to high harmonics in the classical theory. The formal agreement, which is of most importance here, is, of course, unaffected.

which by the rule (12) for the multiplication of Fourier amplitudes is the $(n-m)$ harmonic of $[xy]$, expressed in terms of the action-angle variables.

In the classical theory the Poisson brackets of canonically conjugate variables p_k and q_k satisfy the relations

$$[p_k\ q_l]=\begin{Bmatrix} 1 \text{ when } k=l \\ 0 \text{ when } k\neq l \end{Bmatrix},\ [p_k,\ p_l]=0\ , \qquad [q_k,\ q_l]=0\ .$$

The analogous relations will therefore be assumed for conjugate variables in the quantum theory, that is,

$$\left.\begin{aligned} p_kq_l-q_lp_k &= \begin{Bmatrix} \dfrac{h}{2\pi i}\ 1 \text{ when } k=l \\ 0 \quad \text{ when } k\neq l \end{Bmatrix} \\ p_kp_l-p_lp_k &= 0\ , \\ q_kq_l-q_lq_k &= 0\ . \end{aligned}\right\} \qquad (15)$$

These "exchange relations," by means of which h is introduced into the equations, are of fundamental importance for quantum mechanics. They correspond to the quantum conditions of the theory of stationary classical motions, but whereas these conditions could be applied only to a multiply periodic system, the present exchange relations must be regarded as generally valid for any motion. In fact, as will appear later, they are necessary in order to give meaning to the problem of integration of the equations of motion, which will now be established.

The canonical equations (1) of the classical theory, if expressed in terms of the Poisson brackets, become

$$\dot{p}_k=[Hp_k]\ , \qquad \dot{q}_k=[Hq_k]\ .$$

The simplest assumption is to take over these equations formally into the quantum theory, replacing the Poisson brackets by their quantum analogues. We therefore assume the equations of motion in the quantum theory to be[1]

$$\left.\begin{aligned} \dot{p}_k &= \frac{2\pi i}{h}\,(Hp_k - p_kH)\,, \\ \dot{q}_k &= \frac{2\pi i}{h}\,(Hq_k - q_kH)\,. \end{aligned}\right\} \qquad (16)$$

Clearly the equations (15) and (16) are not independent of each other. Strictly speaking, it is only permissible to assume equation (15) to be true at a single instant of time. The exchange relations at any other time must then be determined by the solution of equations (16); however, a calculation shows that equations (15) are really independent of the time.

The formal basis of the new mechanics is now completed; for any physical application, however, the form of the Hamiltonian corresponding to the special dynamical problem must be known. It is in general sufficient, in the spirit of the correspondence principle, to assume the same form as in the classical theory. The ambiguity as to the

[1] The equations of motion may be written directly in the classical form (1) without the use of the Poisson brackets if partial differentiation is defined in a rational way for matrices. The relations

$$\frac{h}{2\pi i}\frac{\partial f}{\partial q} = pf - fp\,, \qquad \frac{h}{2\pi i}\frac{\partial f}{\partial p} = fq - qf$$

for any function f are then easily established from the exchange relations (15). The more useful form (16) then follows at once.

order of factors in a product which may occur here seldom arises; when it does special considerations suffice to determine the correct form.

The law of the conservation of energy and the Bohr frequency condition are not contained explicitly in the postulates of the theory; it is therefore necessary to show that they may be derived from them. We commence by forming a diagonal matrix W with elements

$$W(nm)=\begin{cases} T_n h & \text{when } n=m \\ 0 & \text{when } n\neq m \end{cases} \tag{17}$$

where the T_n are the term values of equation (5). The time derivative of any quantity x may be expressed in terms of this matrix by the equation

$$\dot{x}=\frac{2\pi i}{h}(Wx-xW)\ , \tag{18}$$

since the (nm) element of $(2\pi i/h)(wx-xw)$ is

$$\frac{2\pi i}{h}\sum_k [W(nk)x(km)-x(nk)W(km)]=2\pi i(T_n-T_m)x(nm)$$
$$=2\pi i\nu(nm)x(nm)=\dot{x}(nm)$$

by equation (10). From equation (18) and the equations of motion (16) it follows that $Wp-pW=Hp-pH$ and $Wq-qW=Hq-qH$, or

$$(W-H)p=p(W-H)\ ,\quad (W-H)q=q(W-H)\ . \tag{18'}$$

That is, the matrix $W-H$ "commutes" with both p and q, and it is readily shown that it therefore commutes with any function of p and q that can be represented as a power series. In particular it commutes with H, so that

$$(W-H)H-H(W-H)=WH-HW=0\ , \tag{19}$$

which, by equation (18), means

$$\dot{H}=0\ , \tag{20}$$

expressing the conservation of energy.

Equation (20) gives for the elements of H the infinite set of equations $\nu(nm)H(nm)=0$. If $\nu(nm)=0$ only when $n=m$, all the non-diagonal elements of H are zero and H is necessarily a diagonal matrix. In this case, the system is said to be "non-degenerate." It may happen, however, that $\nu(nm)=0$ for $n\neq m$; the corresponding elements of H are then undetermined and H is not necessarily diagonal. The system is then said to be "degenerate."

It follows further from equation (18′) that

$$(W_n-H_n)p(nm)=p(nm)(W_m-H_m)\ ,$$
$$(W_n-H_n)q(nm)=q(nm)(W_m-H_m)\ ,$$

i.e., $W_n-H_n=W_m-H_m$ for any value of n and m. Therefore

$$H=W+C\ ,$$

where C is the unity matrix, multiplied by an arbitrary constant. It is most convenient to put

$$H=W\ . \tag{21}$$

The mathematical apparatus belonging to the particle picture has been outlined above. Its physical interpretation is discussed in detail elsewhere, but the two most important rules follow naturally at this point from the correspondence principle.

1. The time average of a quantity represented as a Fourier series is given by the terms independent of t. Hence, for a non-degenerate system, the diagonal elements of the matrix representing any variable give the time averages corresponding to the various stationary states.

2. The radiation process, when the particle picture is used, may be regarded as the emission of photons with the spectral frequencies $\nu(nm)$ accompanied by a simultaneous transition of the atom from the initial state with energy W_n to the final state with energy W_m, $(W_n > W_m)$. The intensity (rate of emission of energy) may then be represented statistically as $A(nm)h\nu(nm)$ where $A(nm)$ is the probability of spontaneous transition from state n to state m with emission of a photon. On the other hand, the classical theory gives for the average intensity corresponding to the τth harmonic $2/3(e^2/c^3)(2\pi)^4[\tau\nu]^4|\boldsymbol{r}_\tau|^2 \cdot 2$ where $e\boldsymbol{r}$ is the vector dipole moment of the electrons ($\boldsymbol{r}$ is the vector with components $x = \sum_k q_k^{(x)}$, $y = \sum_k q_k^{(y)}$, $z = \sum_k q_k^{(z)}$, $q_k^{(x)}$, $q_k^{(y)}$, $q_k^{(z)}$ being the rectangular co-ordinates of the electrons). On equating the expressions of the two theories and replacing Fourier terms by matrix elements we obtain for the transition probability

$$A(nm) = \frac{1}{h\nu(nm)} \frac{2}{3} \frac{e^2}{c^3} [2\pi\nu(nm)]^4 |\boldsymbol{r}(nm)|^2 \cdot 2 . \qquad (22)$$

The justification of this second rule is not obvious since the Maxwell theory also requires reconsideration. However, equation (22) determines only the time average of the emitted radiation, and it has been shown in chapter v, § 4, that the Maxwell theory is competent to furnish this information exactly.

§ 2. THE TRANSFORMATION THEORY

The mathematical scheme of quantum mechanics has been derived in § 1 in a way which displays its analogy to classical mechanics; it is not, however, as yet in an easily usable form. In this section it will be shown that the solution of a dynamical problem in the quantum theory is equivalent to the principal axis transformation of a Hermitian form or tensor. This provides the basis for a practicable method of solution and shows the consistency of the conditions imposed.

Suppose a set of Hermitian matrices p_k, q_k can be found which are independent of the time, satisfy the exchange relations, and make $H(p, q)$ a diagonal matrix. The dynamical problem is then solved, for if the matrices are provided with the time factors $e^{\frac{2\pi i}{h}(H_n - H_m)t}$, where H_n and H_m are the diagonal elements of H, it is readily seen that the equations of motion (16) are satisfied. If $p_k^{(0)}$, $q_k^{(0)}$ is any set of matrices satisfying the exchange relations, the transformations

$$p_k = S^{-1} p_k^{(0)} S \; , \qquad q_k = S^{-1} q_k^{(0)} S \; , \tag{23}$$

where S is any matrix, give a new set likewise satisfying the exchange relations. This is seen algebraically on substituting equations (23) in the exchange relations for the new variables; in a similar way it is easily proved that if f

is any function of the $p_k^{(0)}$ and $q_k^{(0)}$ that can be written as a power series, then

$$f(p_k, q_k) = f(S^{-1}p_k^{(0)}S\ ,\ S^{-1}q_k^{(0)}S) = S^{-1}f(p_k^{(0)},\ q_k^{(0)})S\ . \quad (24)$$

Since special Hermitian matrices satisfying the exchange relations can be found, the problem reduces to that of finding a transformation function S such that

$$S^{-1}H(p_k^{(0)}, q_k^{(0)})S = W\ , \quad (25)$$

where W is a diagonal matrix.

The transformations (23) are analogous to the canonical transformations of classical mechanics; but they have also a geometrical interpretation of great importance if the matrices of the quantum theory are interpreted as tensors in a unitary space of infinitely many dimensions (Hilbert space). This not only furnishes an analytical method of representing the transformations (23) and equation (25) but also provides a convenient language for the physical interpretation of the theory, as shown in chapter iv, § 1. For present purposes a purely abstract formulation will suffice.

Let $u_1^{(0)}$, $u_2^{(0)}$, ... , be an infinite set of unit orthogonal vectors. The space used is that of all vectors

$$t = \sum_n t_n^{(0)} u_n^{(0)}\ ,$$

where the components $t_n^{(0)}$ are complex numbers. A tensor q then expresses a linear relation between two vectors according to the equations

$$t = qs,\ \text{or}\ t_n^{(0)} = \sum_m q^{(0)}(nm) s_m^{(0)}\ .$$

Consider now a transformation from the foregoing co-ordinate system $U_0(u_1^{(0)}, u_2^{(0)}, \ldots)$ to a new co-ordinate system $U(u_1, u_2, \ldots)$, the new vectors being given in terms of the old ones by the linear equations

$$u_n = \sum_m S(mn) u_m^{(0)} . \tag{26}$$

The components t_n of any vector t and $q(nm)$ of any matrix q in the new system are then given by the equations

$$t_n^{(0)} = \sum_m S(nm) t_m , \tag{27}$$

$$q(nm) = \sum_{k,\, l} S^{-1}(nk) q^{(0)}(kl) S(lm) , \tag{28}$$

where S^{-1} is the matrix of the transformation $t_n = \sum_m S^{-1}(nm) t_m^{(0)}$ inverse to equation (27). [S is assumed to be non-singular.] Of special importance are the so-called "unitary" transformations, i.e., those which leave invariant the quadratic form $\sum_n t_n t_n^*$ which is the analogue of distance in unitary space. It is readily verified that for such unitary transformations

$$\sum_k S(nk) S^*(mk) = \sum_k S(kn) S^*(km) = \delta_{nm} ,$$

which means that $S^{-1} = \tilde{S}^*$, or

$$S\tilde{S}^* = \tilde{S}^* S = 1 . \tag{29}$$

They are the analogue in unitary space of rotations of rectangular co-ordinate systems in real, three-dimensional space.

It is now seen that equations (23) are of precisely the form of equations (28), by virtue of the rule (12) for quantum multiplication; p_k, q_k may therefore be regarded as the same matrices or tensors as $p_k^{(0)}$, $q_k^{(0)}$ expressed in a new co-ordinate system U, the new co-ordinates being related to the co-ordinates in the original system U_0 by equations (27). Equation (25) then expresses the condition on the transformation matrix S that in the new system the tensor H is in the diagonal form—i.e., the co-ordinate vectors of the new system are the principal axes of H. It is sufficient to consider only unitary transformations [S satisfying eq. (28)] since under these conditions it is well known that the principal axis transformation problem, at least for finite matrices, always has a solution.

A word is necessary as to the notation. In general it is not expedient to distinguish matrices in different co-ordinate systems by new symbols; they are more conveniently characterized by using a distinguishing letter for the indices of the components in each co-ordinate system. Different numerical values of the indices will be indicated by primes; thus $p(l'l'')$, say, represents the components of p in the "l" system and $p(a'a'')$ the components in another "a" system of co-ordinates. The first of equations (23), for example, is to be written

$$p(a'a'') = \sum_{l'} \sum_{l''} S^{-1}(a'l')p(l'l'')S(l''a'') .$$

The indices of the transformation matrix S then refer naturally to different co-ordinate systems.

The solution of a quantum-mechanical problem given by the equations of motion (16) and the exchange relations (15) thus reduces to the problem of the principal axis transformation of the Hermitian matrix H. It remains to state briefly the method of solution, which is a well-known one. The equation (25) may be written

$$HS - SW = 0\,, \tag{30}$$

which gives for the elements of S the equations

$$\sum_{l''} H(l'l'')S(l''a') - \sum_{a''} S(l'a'')W(a''a') = 0$$
$$\begin{pmatrix} l' = 1, 2, \ldots . \\ a' = 1, 2, \ldots . \end{pmatrix},$$

or, since W is diagonal, an infinite set of homogeneous linear equations

$$\sum_{l''} H(l'l'')S(l''a') - S(l'a')W_{a'} = 0 \quad (l' = 1, 2, \ldots .)\,, \tag{31}$$

for the determination of the elements of any column of the matrix $S(l'a')$. The $W_{a'}$'s, which appear as parameters, are also determined, and, in fact, independently of the $S(l'a')$, since the equations (31) will have a solution when and only when the determinant of the left-hand member is zero, that is, when the $W_{a'}$'s are solutions of the algebraic equation

$$\begin{vmatrix} H(11)-W & H(12) & H(13) & \cdot & \cdot \\ H(21) & H(22)-W & H(23) & \cdot & \cdot \\ H(31) & H(32) & H(33)-W & \cdot & \cdot \\ \cdot & \cdot & \cdot & \cdot & \cdot \\ \cdot & \cdot & \cdot & \cdot & \cdot \\ \cdot & \cdot & \cdot & \cdot & \cdot \end{vmatrix} = 0\,. \tag{32}$$

The roots $W_{a'}$ of this equation are thus characteristic values of equation (30) or equations (31) and are always real. They are the diagonal elements of W and therefore give the energy levels of the system; when the roots of equation (32) are multiple the system is degenerate, for there is then coincidence of frequencies by equation (7).

To each $W_{a'}$ corresponds a characteristic solution $C_{a'}S(1a')$, $C_{a'}S(2a')$, ... , of equations (31) and hence a column of the matrix S, the arbitrary constant $C_{a'}$ occurring because of the homogeneity of the equations (31). In case the system is not degenerate it is readily seen that any two characteristic solutions are orthogonal to each other, i.e.,

$$\sum_{l'} S(l'a')S^*(l'a'') = 0 \qquad \text{when } a' \neq a'' .$$

The relation (29) is thus satisfied for the non-diagonal elements. It may also be satisfied for the diagonal elements by proper choice of the $C_{a'}$, although this "normalization" obviously determines only the absolute magnitude of the $C_{a'}$. There is therefore always an undetermined factor of absolute magnitude one common to the elements of each column of S. In case of degeneracy there is a further indeterminateness, but equation (29) may always be satisfied.

From the transformation function S the co-ordinates and momenta which form the solution are given by equations (23). The extended discussion of the physical interpretation of S is, however, reserved for § 5.

In the preceding it has been tacitly assumed that theorems for finite matrices and sets of equations are true for the infinite ones of quantum mechanics. This may be directly justified only under certain conditions, but the more rigorous treatment shows that the results of the formal treatment above are essentially correct.[1] There is one important distinction, however, in the case of infinite matrices: The characteristic value "spectrum" may contain a continuous sequence of values as well as the discontinuous one hitherto exclusively considered. In the case of the energy this accounts for the existence of continuous optical spectra. The occurrence of continuous characteristic values also means that in certain coordinate systems the elements of the matrices will have continuously variable indices, or indices discontinuous in a certain range and continuous in another. Our matrix relations must accordingly be extended to include this case. The methods of Dirac[2] will be used for this purpose; though somewhat formal in character they have the advantage of great clarity and may be rigorously justified in all cases which occur practically.

In the first place sums must be replaced by integrals in a range where the indices are continuously variable, the elements becoming functions of two sets of variables. Thus when the range is wholly a continuous one the product rule, for example, becomes

$$pq(nm) = \int dk\, p(nk)q(km) \ ,$$

while in the case of mixed ranges there will occur a sum and an integral. To represent the unit matrix in the con-

[1] In many practical problems, however, a principal axis transformation with a finite number of variables suffices, as in the perturbation method (§ 4).

[2] *Proceedings of the Royal Society*, A, **113**, 621, 1927.

tinuous case Dirac has introduced a function $\delta(\xi)$, corresponding to δ_{nm} defined by the following properties:

$$\xi\delta(\xi)=0\ ,$$

so that $\delta(\xi)=0$ for $\xi\neq 0$,

$$\delta(-\xi)=\delta(\xi)\ , \tag{33}$$

and

$$\int_{\xi_1}^{\xi_2}\delta(\xi)d\xi=1\ , \tag{34}$$

when the value zero lies between ξ_1 and ξ_2. It is thus a function with a singularity at $\xi=0$ and is only possible as the limit of a sequence of functions. From the foregoing properties it follows readily that

$$\int_{-\infty}^{+\infty}f(\xi)\delta(a-\xi)d\xi=f(a)\ , \tag{35}$$

$$\int_{-\infty}^{+\infty}f(\xi)\delta'(a-\xi)d\xi=f'(a)\ , \tag{36}$$

where $f(\xi)$ is any regular function and $\delta'(\xi)=(d/d\xi)\delta(\xi)$. Equation (35) results from an integration by parts. Furthermore, since

$$\int_{-\infty}^{+\infty}\delta(a-\xi)\delta(\xi-b)d\xi=0$$

when $a\neq b$ and

$$\int db\int\delta(a-\xi)\delta(\xi-b)d\xi=\int\delta(a-\xi)d\xi\int\delta(\xi-b)db=1\ ,$$

$$\int_{-\infty}^{+\infty}\delta(a-\xi)\delta(\xi-b)d\xi=\delta(a-b)\ , \tag{37}$$

since the integral has all the properties of the δ-function of $a-b$.

The elements of the unit matrix in the continuous case may be expressed in terms of the δ-function, for $\delta(\alpha'-\alpha'')$ has, by equation (37), the property that

$$\int\delta(\alpha'-\alpha''')x(\alpha'''\alpha'')d\alpha'''=x(\alpha'\alpha'') . \qquad (38)$$

Hence

$$1(\alpha'\alpha'')=\delta(\alpha'-\alpha'') .$$

A diagonal matrix with continuous indices is one of the form $q(\alpha'\alpha'')\delta(\alpha'-\alpha'')$. The extension to multiple indices causes no difficulty; the unit matrix, for example, becomes

$$1(\alpha'\alpha'')=\delta(\alpha_1'-\alpha_1'')\delta(\alpha_2'-\alpha_2'') \ldots . \delta(\alpha_f'-\alpha_f'')$$

and may again be written simply $\delta(\alpha'-\alpha'')$.

For the quantum theory those co-ordinate systems in which quantities other than the energy take the diagonal form are also of importance. In such a system it often proves convenient to replace the indices of all matrices by corresponding diagonal elements of matrices which are diagonal in that system. Rows and columns are thus designated by characteristic values of the matrices which define the co-ordinate system. This is equivalent to replacing quantum numbers by the energies of the corresponding stationary states in a system of one degree of freedom; by the energy and, for example, the angular momentum in a system of two degrees of freedom, etc. In general, if the matrices x_1, x_2, ... , x_f have the diagonal form, the matrix elements of q will be written

$$q(x'x'')=q(x_1'x_2' \ldots . x_f' ; \; x_1''x_2'' \ldots . x_f'') ,$$

the primed letters denoting characteristic values of the corresponding matrices; in particular, the diagonal matrices x, when the indices are continuous, have the form

$$x(x'x'') = x'\delta(x_1' - x_1'')\delta(x_2' - x_2'') \dots \delta(x_f' - x_f'') . \quad (39)$$

The question naturally arises as to what matrices can simultaneously have the diagonal form in a given co-ordinate system. The answer is well known from the theory of Hermitian forms, and is highly significant for the quantum theory: Any set of matrices all of which commute with any other of the set can be simultaneously brought to the diagonal form by a unitary transformation. Thus it will always be possible to find a co-ordinate system in which the position co-ordinates $q_1 \dots q_f$ are diagonal, but if the exchange relations are satisfied the momenta $p_1 \dots p_f$ cannot also have the diagonal form.

§ 3. THE SCHRÖDINGER EQUATION

The admission of continuous matrices into the mathematical scheme permits a new formulation of the principal axis transformation problem. If, namely, the original co-ordinate system in which the exchange relations are satisfied is taken to be one in which the q_k are continuous diagonal matrices the equation determining the transformation function S to a system in which any function F is diagonal becomes a partial differential equation, which is the analogue of equations (31). While a rigorous justification of the method used here (that of Dirac[1]) is difficult, the results may be confirmed by more exact, though also more cumbersome, methods.

[1] *Ibid.*

Since the original co-ordinate system need only be one which the co-ordinate matrices are diagonal and bears no necessary relation to any special dynamical problem, we may assume for the q_k the general diagonal form

$$q_k = q_k'\delta(q_1'-q_1'') \dots \delta(q_f'-q_f'') , \tag{40a}$$

the indices being designated by the characteristic values q_k' of q_k. To represent the conjugate momenta a set of matrices must be found which satisfies the exchange relations (15) with the foregoing q_k. A possible set is obtained by taking

$$\left.\begin{aligned} p_k(q'q'') = \frac{h}{2\pi i}\,\delta'(q_k'-q_k'')\delta(q_1'-q_1'') \dots \\ \delta(q_{k-1}'-q_{k-1}'')\delta(q_{k+1}'-q_{k+1}'') \dots \delta(q_f'-q_f'') , \end{aligned}\right\} \tag{40b}$$

for it may be shown by calculating $p_kq_l - q_lp_k$ that the exchange relations are then satisfied. The proof for one degree of freedom is as follows: The $(q'q'')$ element of $pq-qp$ is

$$\frac{h}{2\pi i}\int dq'''[\delta'(q'-q''')q'''\delta(q'''-q'')-q'\delta(q'-q''')\delta'(q'''-q'')] .$$

The first term, on integration by parts, becomes

$$\int dq'''\delta(q'-q''')\frac{\partial}{\partial q'''}[q'''\delta(q'''-q'')]$$
$$=\int dq'''[q'''\delta'(q'''-q'')\delta(q'-q''')+\delta(q'-q''')\delta(q'''-q'')] .$$

Therefore,

$$(pq-qp)(q'q'') = \frac{h}{2\pi i}\int dq'''[(q'''-q')\delta(q'-q''')\delta'(q'''-q'')]$$
$$+\frac{h}{2\pi i}\int \delta(q'-q''')\delta(q'''-q'')dq''' .$$

The first integral vanishes by equation (33), while the second is $(h/2\pi i)\delta(q'-q'')$ by equation (37). Hence

$$(pq-qp)(q'q'')=\left(\frac{h}{2\pi i}\right)\delta(q'-q'')=\left(\frac{h}{2\pi i}\right)1(q'q'')$$

and the exchange relations are satisfied. The extension to several degrees of freedom follows without difficulty.

Consider now the general problem of transforming any function $F(p, q)$ to the diagonal form by a unitary transformation S. As in the discontinuous case S is essentially determined by equation (25), which now becomes

$$S^{-1}FS=F'\delta(F'-F'') ,$$

the indices in the new system where F is diagonal being denoted by F' and F''. Again this may be written in the form of equation (30):

$$FS=S[F'\delta(F'-F'')]$$

or

$$\int F(q'q'')S(q''F')dq''=S(q'F')F' , \tag{41}$$

which is an integral equation corresponding to the infinite set of linear equations (31). This, however, becomes a partial differential equation when the particular values of p_k, q_k given by equations (40) are substituted in the left-hand member. Carrying out the integration, using the properties of the δ-functions, gives

$$\int F(p_k, q_k)(q'q'')S(q''F')dq''=F\left(\frac{h}{2\pi i}\frac{\partial}{\partial q_k'}, q_k'\right)S(q'F') , \tag{42}$$

where $F([h/2\pi i][\partial/\partial q_k'], q_k')$ is the operator obtained from F by the substitution

$$p_k \to \frac{h}{2\pi i}\frac{\partial}{\partial q_k'}\,, \qquad q_k \to q_k'\,. \tag{43}$$

Only the proof for one degree of freedom need be given. For the special cases $F=q$ and $F=p$ the result follows at once, since by equations (36) and (35)

$$\int \frac{h}{2\pi i}\delta'(q'-q'')S(q''F')dq''=\frac{h}{2\pi i}\frac{\partial S(q'F')}{\partial q'}\,,$$

$$\int q'\delta(q'-q'')S(q''F')dq''=q'S(q'F')\,.$$

Since all functions which need be considered can be built up by multiplication and addition from p and q, it only remains to show that if equation (42) holds for F_1 and F_2 it holds for F_1+F_2 and F_1F_2. That it holds for F_1+F_2 is trivial. For $F_1F_2=\int F_1(q'q'')\,F(q'''q'')dq'''$ substitution in equation (42) gives

$$\begin{aligned}
&\int\int F_1(q'q''')dq'''F_2(q'''q'')dq''S(q''F')\\
&=\int F_1(q'q''')dq'''\int F_2(q'''q'')S(q''F')dq''\,,\\
&=\int F_1(q'q''')dq'''F_2\left(\frac{h}{2\pi i}\frac{\partial}{\partial q'''}\,,\ q'''\right)S(q'''F')\,,\\
&=F_1\left(\frac{h}{2\pi i}\frac{\partial}{\partial q'}\,,\ q'\right)F_2\left(\frac{h}{2\pi i}\frac{\partial}{\partial q'}\,,\ q'\right)S(q'F')\,,\\
&=F_1F_2\left(\frac{h}{2\pi i}\frac{\partial}{\partial q'}\,,\ q'\right)S(q'F')\,,
\end{aligned}$$

and the theorem is therefore proved.

The required transformation function $S(q'F')$ must therefore be a solution of the partial differential equation

$$F\left(\frac{h}{2\pi i}\frac{\partial}{\partial q_k'}, q_k'\right)S(q'F') - F'S(q'F') = 0 , \qquad (44)$$

in which F' is a parameter, corresponding to $W_{a'}$ in equations (31) of which equation (44) is the analogue. Here also there will be only certain discrete values or continuous ranges of F for which a solution is possible; these characteristic values give the diagonal elements of F. The conditions that the transformation be unitary($\tilde{S}^* = S^{-1}$) are of importance in determining the character of the solutions of equation (44). When S is continuous in both indices they may be written

$$\int S^*(q'F')S(q'F'')dq' = \delta(F' - F'') , \qquad (45)$$

$$\int S^*(q'F')S(q''F')dF' = \delta(q' - q'') , \qquad (46)$$

analogously to equations (28). There are corresponding summations when the characteristic value spectrum contains a discrete part.

The mathematical problem just treated is a very general one. That there are corresponding physical ones will appear after the extended physical interpretation of the transformation function has been given in § 5. For the present we only note that the foregoing method, when applied to the Hamiltonian H, yields a solution of the equations of motion.

When H is substituted for F in equation (44) the resulting differential equation is the Schrödinger[1] equation,

[1] E. Schrödinger, *Annalen der Physik*, **79**, 361, 489, 1926.

originally discovered in an entirely different manner. The corresponding transformation function $S(q'H')$ is in this case customarily written $\psi_W(q)$. The Schrödinger equation is then

$$H\left(\frac{h}{2\pi i}\frac{\partial}{\partial q_k},\ q_k\right)\psi_W(q)-W\psi_W(q)=0 \qquad (47)$$

and its characteristic values given the energy levels of the system.

The solutions $\psi_W(q)$ form the columns of the transformation matrix, which should be compared with the S of § 2. Both represent transformations to a system in which the energy is diagonal—in the present case, however, the initial system is a particular one in which the co-ordinates are diagonal, corresponding to a particular choice of $p_k^{(0)}$, $q_k^{(0)}$ in § 2.

In the typical case of a discrete characteristic value spectrum the orthogonality conditions (45) become

$$\int\psi^*_{W'}(q)\psi_{W''}(q)dq=0 \qquad (48)$$

when $W'\neq W''$,

$$\int|\psi_W(q)|^2dq=1\ . \qquad (49)$$

Equation (49) is in general equivalent to boundary conditions, and the orthogonality of the characteristic solutions $\psi_W(q)$, which usually follows, then assures the validity of equations (48). As in the case of the transformation matrix S of § 2 there remains in each "column" $\psi_W(q)$ an undetermined phase factor $e^{i\varphi_W}$ not fixed by the normalization (49).

The co-ordinate and momentum matrices in the sy... in which the energy is diagonal are, by equations ...

$$p(W'W'')=\int\psi^*_{W'}\frac{h}{2\pi i}\frac{\partial\psi_{W''}}{\partial q}dq\ , \qquad (5$$

$$q(W'W'')=\int\psi^*_{W'}(q)q\psi_{W''}(q)dq\ . \qquad (51$$

Equations (47), (50), and (51) constitute the most effective mathematical method for treatment of the dynamical problems of quantum mechanics, but they contribute nothing new to the physical interpretation. Special considerations are necessary to make clear the physical meaning of the transformation matrix (cf. § 5).

§ 4. THE PERTURBATION METHOD

A description of the principal features of the perturbation theory in quantum mechanics is necessary at this point. This method may be used when the Hamiltonian H can be developed in terms of a small parameter λ in the form

$$H=H_0+\lambda H_1+\lambda^2 H_2+\ \dots\ , \qquad (52)$$

and the solution of the problem corresponding to the Hamiltonian H_0 is known, i.e., when the matrices p and q, and any function of p and q, are known in that system in which H_0 is diagonal (H_0-system). In the following the letter H will be used for the energy matrix in this co-ordinate system, while W will stand for the energy matrix in the system in which the complete Hamiltonian is diagonal (H-system). Corresponding to equation (52) W may be written in the form

$$W=W_0+\lambda W_1+\lambda^2 W_2+\ \dots\ . \qquad (53)$$

ere $W_0=H_0$. The required transformation function ich leads from the H_0-system to the H-system may also written

$$S=S_0+\lambda S_1+\lambda^2 S_2+\ldots\ldots, \tag{54}$$

nd S will be unitary to zeroth approximation if

$$S_0\tilde{S}_0^*=1 . \tag{55}$$

A set of equations will now be found from which S may be determined. As in § 2, S must satisfy the equation $HS=SW$, W being diagonal; substituting the developments (52), (53), and (54) in this equation and equating coefficients of equal powers of λ gives the equations

$$\left.\begin{array}{l} H_0S_0=S_0W_0 , \\ H_0S_1-S_1H_0=S_0W_1 , \\ H_0S_2-S_2H_0+H_2S_2-S_1W_1=S_0W_2 , \\ \quad\vdots \\ H_0S_r-S_rH_0+F_r(S_1\ldots\ldots S_{r-1}, H_1\ldots\ldots H_r)=S_0W_r , \\ \quad\vdots \end{array}\right\} \tag{56}$$

which may be solved in sequence for S_0, S_1, ... , and W_0, W_1, ...

The first equation gives, for the elements of S_0,

$$S_0(nn)[H_0(nn)-H_0(mm)]=S_0(nm)h\nu_0(nm)=0 , \tag{57}$$

where the $\nu_0(nm)$ are the frequencies of the unperturbed system.[1] A distinction must be made at this point be-

[1] For simplicity it is assumed that all matrices are discontinuous in their indices. The method is equally applicable for continuous indices and hence for the Schrödinger equation.

tween non-degenerate and degenerate unperturbed systems. In the former case [$\nu_0(nm) \neq 0$ when $n \neq m$] it follows at once from equation (57) that S_0 is a diagonal matrix; in the latter the non-diagonal terms of S_0 do not necessarily vanish. Since the treatment of the two cases differs from here on it will be assumed at first that the unperturbed system is non-degenerate.

When S_0 is diagonal, equation (55) requires $|S_0(nm)| = 1$; hence, disregarding the undetermined phases always present in S, we may take $S_0 = 1$. The second of equations (56) then becomes

$$H_0 S_1 - S_1 H_0 + H_1 = W_1 ,$$

or, for the elements

$$h\nu_0(nm) S_1(nm) + H_1(mm) = W_1(nm)\delta_{nm} . \qquad (58)$$

For the diagonal elements this gives the determination of the perturbation energy to first approximation:

$$W_1(nn) = H_1(nn) . \qquad (59)$$

When $n \neq m$ equation (58) determines the non-diagonal elements of S_1; the diagonal elements of S_1 are undetermined by equation (58) but the condition $S\tilde{S}^* = 1$ is satisfied to first approximation if they are taken to be zero. Hence

$$S_1(nm) = -\frac{H_1(nm)}{h\nu_0(nm)} (1 - \delta_{nm}) .$$

The similarity of these results to those of the perturbation theory in classical mechanics will be noted. In particular equation (59) corresponds to the well-known classical theorem that the perturbation function is to first order the average of the perturbation energy, since the diagonal elements of H_1 are its time average. The equation may accordingly be written

$$W_1 = \overline{H}_1 .$$

The remaining equations in (56), when treated in the same way, give

$$W_r(nn) = F_r(nn) ,$$

$$S_r(nm) = -\frac{F_r(nm)}{h\nu_0(nm)} (1-\delta_{nm}) ,$$

each F_r being determined by the equations preceding the rth one.

If the unperturbed solution is degenerate it no longer follows from $W_0 S_0 = S_0 W_0$ that S_0 is diagonal. When, for example, $W_0(n+1) = W_0(n+2) = \ldots = W_0(n+k)$, equation (57) shows that S_0 can still contain elements that correspond to transitions between the states $n+1$, $n+2$, $\ldots$, $n+k$. The second of equations (56), however, provides a system of homogeneous linear equations giving these non-vanishing elements of S_0 and at the same time W_1. Again forming the time mean over the unperturbed motion (i.e., picking out the rows n and columns m for which the corresponding $\nu(nm)$ vanish) gives the equation

$$\overline{H}_1 S_0 = S_0 W_1 , \qquad (60)$$

which provides a system of homogeneous linear equations precisely analogous to equations (31). As there W_1 may be found independently of S_0 from the so-called "secular equation,"

$$\begin{vmatrix} H_1(n+1, n+1)-W_1 & \cdots & H_1(n+1, n+k) \\ H_1(n+2, n+1) & \cdots & H_1(n+2, n+k) \\ \vdots & & \\ H_1(n+k, n+1) & \cdots & H_1(n+k, n+k)-W_1 \end{vmatrix} = 0. \quad (61)$$

The roots give the elements of W_1 and the corresponding linear equations determine S_0 except for a phase factor in each column. From here on the calculation may be carried out as for a non-degenerate system.

§ 5. RESONANCE BETWEEN TWO ATOMS: THE PHYSICAL INTERPRETATION OF THE TRANSFORMATION MATRICES

The completed scheme for the interpretation of the mathematics of the quantum theory depends on certain assumptions as to the physical meaning of the transformation functions. To illustrate the nature of these assumptions and to make them plausible a simple problem will first be discussed—that of the interaction of two atoms in resonance.[1]

Consider two atoms, I and II, with the characteristic value spectra $W_I(n)$ and $W_{II}(i)$ which have a common characteristic frequency, so that, for instance, $\nu_I(nm) = \nu_{II}(ik)$ or $W_I(n)-W_I(m)=W_{II}(i)-W_{II}(k)$; they are thus in resonance. An energy interchange can then occur between the two atoms, even if the coupling between them

[1] W. Heisenberg, *Zeitschrift für Physik*, **40**, 501, 1926.

is very weak, the interaction taking place as follows: Atom I goes from the state n to the state m, giving up energy $h\nu(nm)$, while atom II takes up the same energy $h\nu(nm) = h\nu(ik)$ in going from state k to state i, the process being reversible.

If the uncoupled atoms are considered as the "unperturbed" system the interaction energy H_1 may be treated as a perturbation by the method of § 4. A state of the combined atoms, in the system in which $W_I + W_{II}$ is diagonal, may be specified by two integers (nk), the first giving the state of atom I, the second the state of atom II. The states (nk) and (mi) of the unperturbed system then have equal energies by virtue of the relation

$$W_0(nk) = W_I(n) + W_{II}(k) = W_I(m) + W_{II}(i) = W_0(mi) \quad (62)$$

resulting from the equality of frequencies; the resonance thus introduces a characteristic degeneracy. The secular equation for the determination of the perturbation W_1 in the energy may be set up as in § 2 by picking out the elements of the interaction energy $H_1(nk;\, mi)$ for which the frequencies $\nu(nk;\, mi) = (1/h)[W_0(nk) + W_0(mi)]$ vanish by equation (62). This gives, corresponding to equation (61),

$$\begin{vmatrix} H_1(nk;\, nk) - W_1 & H_1(nk;\, mi) \\ H_1(mi;\, nk) & H_1(mi;\, mi) - W_1 \end{vmatrix} = 0\,. \quad (63)$$

The two solutions of this quation are the perturbation energies $W_1(a)$ and $W_1(b)$ of the two states of the coupled system which replace the states (nk) and (mi) of equal energy for the uncoupled system. (The more symmetric notation $W(nk;\, mi)$, etc., is likely to lead to confusion, since there is not one-to-one correspondence with the unperturbed states.) To each root of equation (63) corresponds a column of the transformation matrix S (obtained by solution of the linear equations) which will be of the form

$$\left.\begin{aligned} S(nk;\, a) &= s(nk;\, a)e^{i\phi_a} \\ S(mi;\, a) &= s(mi;\, a)e^{i\phi_a} \end{aligned}\right\} \text{ for } W_1(a)\ ,$$

$$\left.\begin{aligned} S(nk;\, b) &= s(nk;\, b)e^{i\phi_b} \\ S(mi;\, b) &= s(mi;\, b)e^{i\phi_b} \end{aligned}\right\} \text{ for } W_1(b)\ .$$

The ϕ's are real quantities undetermined by the "normalization" $S\tilde{S}^* = 1$. The orthogonal matrix

$$S = \begin{Vmatrix} s(nk;\, a)e^{i\phi_a} & s(nk;\, b)e^{i\phi_b} \\ s(mi;\, a)e^{i\phi_a} & s(mi;\, b)e^{i\phi_b} \end{Vmatrix} \tag{64}$$

is thus the zeroth approximation to the transformation function leading from the system in which the energies W_I and W_{II} are diagonal to the system in which the total energy $W_I + W_{II} = W$ is diagonal.

It may be noted parenthetically that in the case of two equivalent atoms resonance will always occur. This special case is obtained from the foregoing by setting $i = n$ and $k = m$; it is then readily shown that

$$H_1(nm;\, nm) = H_1(mn;\, mn)\ ,$$

$$H_1(nm;\, mn) = H_1(mn;\, nm)\ ,$$

when the interaction is symmetric in the two systems. Since H_1 is Hermitian the non-diagonal terms in the determinant of equation (63) are real, and the solutions are seen to be

$$\left.\begin{aligned} W_1(a) &= H_1(nm;\, nm) + H_1(mn;\, nm)\ , \\ W_1(b) &= H_1(nm;\, nm) - H_1(mn;\, nm)\ . \end{aligned}\right\} \qquad (65)$$

For the corresponding matrix of the s's the calculation gives, after normalization,

$$\begin{array}{c} \\ nm \\ \\ mn \end{array} \begin{array}{c} \begin{array}{cc} (a) & (b) \end{array} \\ \left\| \begin{array}{cc} \frac{1}{\sqrt{2}} & -\frac{1}{\sqrt{2}} \\ \frac{1}{\sqrt{2}} & \frac{1}{\sqrt{2}} \end{array} \right\| \end{array} . \qquad (66)$$

We return now to the general case.

We shall next discuss the further physical information that may be obtained from these results. Consider, for instance, the question of what may be said in the quantum theory as to the energy of atom I alone as a function of the time. Classically there would occur between two coupled oscillators of equal frequency a periodic and harmonic energy interchange with a frequency proportional to the coupling force; the energy of one of the oscillators would be given by a curve like that of Figure 19*a*. In the quantum theory, on the other hand, it is to be expected that the energy of atom I has either the value $W_I(n)$ or $W_I(m)$, with a probability of transition between these values depending again on the strength of coupling; $H_I(t)$ should therefore be represented by a curve like that of Figure 19*b*. To be sure, this curve cannot be calculated in the quantum theory, nor can it be experimentally determined; nevertheless the rules so far obtained for the physical interpretation of quantum mechanics are sufficient to permit a calculation of the time mean and the mean-square fluctuations of $H_I(t)$ or any function of $H_I(t)$.

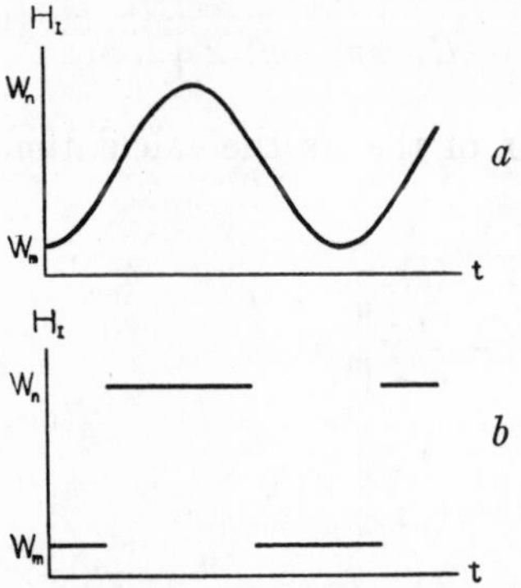

FIG. 19

The calculation of the time mean of any function of $H_I(t)$ may be made as follows. By rule 1 of § 1 the diagonal elements of the matrix representing any quantity give directly the time averages in the corresponding states. The average $\overline{f(H_I)_a}$ in the state a may therefore be calculated in terms of the diagonal elements $f(W_I(n))$ and $f(W_I(m))$ of $f(H_I)$ in the system in which H_I is itself diagonal (the unperturbed system) by making use of the transformation function S of equation (64):

$$\left.\begin{aligned}\overline{f(H_I)_a}&=[f(H_I)](aa)=S^*(nk;\,a)f(nk;\,nk)S(nk;\,a)\\&\qquad\qquad+S^*(mi;\,a)f(mi;\,mi)S(mi;\,a)\\&=|S(nk;\,a)|^2f(W_I(n)(n))+|S(mi;\,a)|^2f(W_I(m))\,.\end{aligned}\right\}\quad(67)$$

This is precisely the expression for the time average which would result from the assumption that $f(H_I)$ can have only the values $f(W_I(n))$ and $f(W_I(m))$ and that these values occur with relative frequencies $|S(nk;\,a)|^2$ and $|S(mi;\,a)|^2$, respectively. Since $f(W_I(n))$ and $f(W_I(m))$ are the elements of $f(H_I)$ in the system in which $f(H_I)$ is diagonal, the first part of the foregoing assumption is equivalent to the hypothesis that the possible values of f are the diagonal elements of its matrix in the system in which it is itself diagonal. The second part, on the other hand, is a consequence of supposing that $|S(nk;\, a)|^2$ is the relative probability of finding the value $f(W_I(n))$ for $f(H_I)$ when the total system is in the state a. (The index (nk) corresponds to the value $f(W_I(n))$ since it is the label of a stationary state in the system in which f is diagonal.) The interpretation as relative probabilities is consistent because by the normalization $|S(nk;\, a)|^2+|S(mi;\, a)|^2=1$.

While a special problem has been treated here the formal relations are the same in the general transformation problem. Thus if $S(\alpha'\beta')$ is the transformation matrix from a system in which any quantity α is diagonal to a system in which β is diagonal[1] the time average of $f(\alpha)$ will always appear in the form (67); i.e.,

$$f(\alpha)_{\beta'}=[f(\alpha)](\beta'\beta')=\sum_{\alpha'} S^*(\alpha'\beta')[f(\alpha)](\alpha'\alpha')S(\alpha'\beta')$$

$$=\sum_{\alpha'} |S(\alpha'\beta')|^2 f_\alpha(\alpha'\alpha')$$

is the time average of $f(\alpha)$ corresponding to the state β'. It is therefore reasonable to generalize the assumptions made above in a special case and to make the following hypotheses as regards the physical interpretation of the transformation scheme:[2]

The values which a quantity α *can take on are given by*

[1] The practice of labeling rows and columns by the elements of the diagonal matrices is used here again.

[2] P. Jordan, *Zeitschrift für Physik*, **40**, 809, 1927; **44**, 1, 1927; P. A. M. Dirac, *Proceedings of the Royal Society*, A, **113**, 621, 1927.

its characteristic value spectrum, i.e., by the elements of its matrix in the system in which it is itself diagonal.

If $S(\alpha'\beta')$ *is the unitary transformation matrix from a system in which* α *is diagonal to a system in which* β *is diagonal then*

$$|S(\alpha'\beta')|^2 \tag{68}$$

is the relative probability of finding the value α' *of* α *when it is known that the value* β' *must be ascribed to* β.

The foregoing assumptions of course apply equally well to the case of continually varying indices and hence to the case in which S is found by solution of a Schrödinger equation.

The detailed discussion of the physical interpretation of the statistical elements thus introduced into the theory will be found in the body of the text and especially in chapter iv. Here it will only be noted that we must add the express condition that the experiment under consideration actually affords a determination of α'. At first sight this condition appears trivial; it is, however, essential, for an application of the foregoing interpretation of the quantities (68) without consideration of the experiment leading to the measurement of α' gives rise at once to logical inconsistencies.

Having established the basis for its physical interpretation, we proceed to the further development of the general transformation theory.

The elements of the transformation matrix S give probabilities only on forming the squares of their absolute magnitudes; they may themselves be called "probability amplitudes." Carrying out successively a transformation from the system α (the system in which α is diagonal) to a system β and then a transformation from the system β to the system γ gives, since transformations combine by the rule for matrix multiplication,

$$S(\alpha'\gamma') = \sum_{\beta'} S(\alpha'\beta')S(\beta'\gamma') \,. \tag{69}$$

Thus quite independently of γ the probability amplitude $S(\alpha'\gamma')$ can always be represented as a linear function of the set of probability amplitudes $S(\alpha'\beta')$. The probability amplitude for finding α' regardless of the predetermined quantity γ', which may be written simply $S(\alpha')$, is therefore, even in the most general case, a linear function of the elements of the transformation matrix $S(\alpha'\beta')$, and the system β may be chosen arbitrarily. In particular β may be taken to be the energy, and $S(\alpha')$ can then always be expressed in the form

$$S(\alpha') = \sum_{W'} c_{W'} S_{W'}(\alpha') \,, \tag{70}$$

where the $c_{W'}$'s are constants and $S_{W'}(\alpha')$ is the transformation matrix to the system in which W is diagonal.

While the probabilities $S_{W'}(\alpha')$ are always constant in time, referring to a *stationary* state W', this is not true in general for $|S(\alpha')|^2$ (i.e., when something other than the energy is specified). The proper time dependence of $S(\alpha')$ may be deduced from the following considerations:

According to (9) each matrix element $x(nm)$ has a time

factor $e^{\frac{2\pi i}{h}(W_n - W_m)t}$ in the system in which the energy is diagonal. Since on transforming to this system from any other system

$$x(nm) = \sum_{\alpha'\alpha''} S^*(\alpha' n) x(\alpha'\alpha'') S(\alpha'' m) \ , \qquad (71)$$

the correct time dependence will be obtained by providing each element $S(\alpha' n)$ with the time factor $e^{-\frac{2\pi i}{h} W_n t}$. This is possible since hitherto $S(\alpha' n)$ has contained an arbitrary phase factor of absolute magnitude 1; from now on it will be understood that $S(\alpha' n) = S_{W'}(\alpha')$ contains this time factor.

The most general probability amplitude $S(\alpha')$, since it can be expressed in the form (70), must satisfy the equation $HS - SW = 0$ determining the $S_{W'}(\alpha')$. Since $SW = -(h/2\pi i)(\partial S/\partial t)$ when S has the time factor introduced above, the equation for $S(\alpha')$ becomes

$$\sum_{\alpha''} H(\alpha'\alpha'') S(\alpha'') + \frac{h}{2\pi i} \frac{\partial S(\alpha')}{\partial t} = 0 \ . \qquad (72)$$

In particular taking α to be a co-ordinate q, this becomes the wave equation of Schrödinger,

$$H\left(\frac{h}{2\pi i}\frac{\partial}{\partial q}, q\right)\psi(q) + \frac{h}{2\pi i}\frac{\partial \psi(q)}{\partial t} = 0 \ . \qquad (73)$$

Characteristic solutions of the form $\psi_{W'}(q) = u_{W'}(q) e^{-\frac{2\pi i}{h} W' t}$ correspond to the elements $S_{W'}(\alpha')$ with the time factor, and by (70) the most general probability amplitude is

$$\psi = \sum_{W'} c_{W'} u_{W'} e^{-\frac{2\pi i}{h} W' t} \qquad (74)$$

As an example of the application of equation (72) consider again the example of coupled atoms. Suppose a measurement at time $t=0$ gives the result that atom I is in state n and atom II in state k. Equation (72) then gives the variation with time of the matrix S given by equation (64), in which the time is contained only in the phases ϕ_a and ϕ_b. Substitution in equation (72), since the matrix s of the constant amplitudes satisfies the equation $Hs+sW=0$, gives

$$\frac{h}{2\pi i}\frac{\partial\phi_a}{\partial t}=-W_a\,,\qquad \frac{h}{2\pi i}\frac{\partial\phi_b}{\partial t}=-W_b\,.$$

Hence $\phi_a=-2\pi i/h\cdot W_a t+\text{Const.}$ and $\phi_b=-2\pi i/h\cdot W_b t+\text{Const.}$ and the characteristic solutions of equation (70) are $S(nk;a)=\text{Const.}\times s(nk;a)e^{-\frac{2\pi i}{h}W_a t}$, etc. The general probability amplitudes are then by equation (70),

$$S(nk)=c_a s(nk;\,a)e^{-\frac{2\pi i}{h}W_a t}+c_b s(nk;\,b)e^{-\frac{2\pi i}{h}W_b t}\,,$$

$$S(mi)=c_a s(mi;\,a)e^{-\frac{2\pi i}{h}W_a t}+c_b s(mi;\,b)e^{-\frac{2\pi i}{h}W_b t}\,,$$

where the c's are constants which may be determined by the initial conditions. Since in this case the initial conditions are $S(nk)=1$, $S(mi)=0$, and the determinant of the s's is 1, we readily find

$$S(nk)=s(mi;\,b)s(nk;\,a)e^{-\frac{2\pi i}{h}W_a t}-s(mi;\,a)s(nk;\,b)e^{-\frac{2\pi i}{h}W_b t}\,,$$

$$S(mi)=s(mi;\,b)s(mi;\,b)\left[e^{-\frac{2\pi i}{h}W_a t}-e^{-\frac{2\pi i}{h}W_b t}\right].$$

For the special case of equivalent atoms, where s has the form (66),

$$S(nm)=\frac{1}{2}\left(e^{-\frac{2\pi i}{h}W_a t}+e^{-\frac{2\pi i}{h}W_b t}\right)$$

$$S(mn)=\frac{1}{2}\left(e^{-\frac{2\pi i}{h}W_a t}-e^{-\frac{2\pi i}{h}W_b t}\right).$$

From this follow the probabilities

$$|S(nm)|^2=\frac{1}{2}\left[1+\cos\frac{2\pi}{h}(W_a-W_b)t\right]$$

$$|S(mn)|^2=\frac{1}{2}\left[1-\cos\frac{2\pi}{h}(W_a-W_b)t\right].$$

These formulas give the probabilities of finding (nm) or (mn) as functions of the time. As W_a-W_b is small to the order of magnitude of the interaction energy of the atoms, the probabilities vary only slowly. Shortly after the first measurement (i.e., for small values of t) it is extremely probable that we find again the configuration (nm). If, however, the second measurement is made exactly at time $t=\frac{1}{2}h(W_a-W_b)$, the result will certainly be the configuration (mn). All of these considerations are valid only when the system actually remains unperturbed in the interval between the two measurements; that is, actually remains governed by equation (72). This condition is, of course, quite trivial. It is specially mentioned here, however, as it is of decisive importance for the consistency of the theory.

The interpretation of the transformation matrices as probability functions just sketched gives a complete scheme for the application of the mathematics of the quantum mechanics to all physical problems.

§ 6. THE CORPUSCULAR CONCEPT FOR RADIATION

The corpuscular theory of radiation is too well known in its general outlines to require extended discussion at this point. It is essentially Einstein's theory of light quanta according to which radiation can be regarded as the action of rapidly moving particles (quanta) whose velocity is always c. Energy E and momentum p are related by the fundamental equation

$$E=cp\ , \tag{75}$$

and the color is given by the quantum relation

$$\nu=\frac{E}{h}\ .$$

Light quanta can appear and disappear, so that in contradistinction to the particle picture of matter their number is variable. No interaction takes place between different light quanta (when gravitation is disregarded), but the interaction between light quanta and matter is responsible for the phenomena of absorption, emission, and dispersion.

§ 7. QUANTUM STATISTICS

Consider a system of n identical particles that are entirely indistinguishable from each other (e.g., electrons or photons). For simplicity it will be assumed that the system has only a discrete characteristic value spectrum, and the interaction between the particles will at first be neglected. The problem may be treated by first determining the possible states and corresponding characteristic functions $\psi_a(r)$ for the individual particles and then considering the distribution of the n particles among these states. In order to treat such a statistical distribution it is necessary to define what constitutes a distinct state of the system.

In classical statistics (Boltzmann statistics) a distribution of n particles among n different states has a relative probability $n!$, since obviously every permutation of the n particles represents an independent realization of the given distribution. In the quantum theory this means that every distribution of n particles among n different states corresponds to an $n!$-fold degenerate term of the total system. The corresponding $n!$ linearly independent characteristic functions are obtained by performing the $n!$ permutations of the r_{β_k} with the a_i fixed, in the expression

$$\psi_{a_1}(r_{\beta_1})\psi_{a_2}(r_{\beta_2}) \ldots \psi_{a_n}(r_{\beta_n}) \, . \tag{76}$$

Instead of the functions (76) any other system of $n!$ linearly independent linear aggregates may of course be used to describe the n-body problem. One is led to such a system of functions, for example, on attempting to treat the interaction of the particles as a perturbation. Among the $n!$ linear aggregates thus obtained two are singled out by a particularly simple structure:

$$\sum_{\substack{\text{All} \\ \text{permutations}}} \psi_{a_1}(r_1)\psi_{a_2}(r_2) \ldots \psi_{a_n}(r_n) \, , \tag{77}$$

and the determinant

$$|\psi_{a_i}(r_k)| \qquad (i, k = 1, 2, \ldots, n) \, . \tag{78}$$

The first is unaltered by any interchange of two particles and is called the "symmetric characteristic function" of the system; the second only changes its sign on such an interchange and is called the "antisymmetric characteristic function." If it is assumed that the ψ_a's are normalized, then it is readily shown that the characteristic functions (77) and (78) of the total system are also normalized if multiplied by $\sqrt{1/n!}$.

These relations are clearly illustrated in the simplest case of $n=2$. Corresponding to one particle in state a_1 and the other in state a_2, there is then a doubly degenerate term with the two characteristic functions

$$\psi_s(1, 2)=\frac{1}{\sqrt{2}}\,[\psi_{a_1}(r_1)\psi_{a_2}(r_2)+\psi_{a_1}(r_2)\psi_{a_2}(r_1)]\,,$$

$$\psi_a(1, 2)=\frac{1}{\sqrt{2}}\,[\psi_{a_1}(r_1)\psi_{a_2}(r_2)-\psi_{a_1}(r_2)\psi_{a_2}(r_1)]\,.$$

In the first place it is readily seen that no intercombinations can take place between terms with symmetric and terms with antisymmetric characteristic functions. The probability of such a transition is always given by an integral of the form

$$\int f(1, 2)\psi_s(1, 2)\psi_a(1, 2)d\tau_1 d\tau_2 \qquad (79)$$

in which $f(1, 2)$ is a function which is not altered when the particles are interchanged, since the two particles are indistinguishable. If now the two electrons are interchanged in (79) the value of the integral is clearly unaltered, since it is only the designation of the variables of integration that is changed. On the other hand, the sign of $\psi_a(1, 2)$

is reversed while all other quantities in the integrand remain the same. Accordingly (79) must vanish.

A more thorough mathematical investigation based on the theory of the representation of groups shows that this special result must be generalized to the following:[1]

The terms of a system of *n* equal particles may always be divided into partial systems in such a way that only the terms belonging to a given partial system can combine with each other. In particular, there will always occur two partial systems in one of which the characteristic functions are symmetric, while in the other they are antisymmetric.

This result remains valid for any interaction between the particles provided only that the interaction of the particles is a symmetric function of their co-ordinates.

The fact that intercombinations cannot occur between two different term systems leaves open the possibility of introducing further hypotheses which exclude all but one of these systems from physical significance.

Consider, for example, the symmetric term system alone. A definite distribution of the particles among the individual states of the single particles (again neglecting the interaction) corresponds, in this term system, to only a single characteristic function. The possibilities that are represented in the symmetric term system therefore correspond to those states which are distinguished in the Bose-Einstein[2] statistics.

In the term system made up of antisymmetric char-

[1] E. Wigner, *Zeitschrift für Physik*, **40**, 883, 1927.

[2] S. N. Bose, *ibid.*, **26**, 178, 1924; A. Einstein, *Berliner Berichte*, p. 261, 1924.

acteristic functions, on the other hand, any function which corresponds to two particles in the same state necessarily vanishes. This is the expression in the quantum theory of the Pauli[1] exclusion of equivalent orbits, which applies to electrons and protons. The choice of an antisymmetric term system corresponds to the use of the Fermi[2]-Dirac[3] statistics.

Quantum statistics thus singles out one term system from the possible term manifolds of an n-body problem, of either symmetric or antisymmetric characteristic functions, as the only physically significant one; each term of the manifold thus singled out represents a distinct state of the physical system of n-bodies. The first case corresponds to the Bose-Einstein statistics, which applies to light quanta; the second to the Pauli-Fermi-Dirac statistics. It is important to remember that this formulation remains valid for any interaction of the particles.

In applying the Pauli exclusion principle to electrons or protons it must not be forgotten that r_k, in $\psi_a(r_k)$, represents not only the three space co-ordinates of the kth particle, but also the fourth variable describing the spin which can only have the values $+\frac{1}{2}$ and $-\frac{1}{2}$.

The formulation of quantum statistics in the wave picture will be treated in § 10.

§ 8. THE WAVE CONCEPT FOR MATTER AND RADIATION: CLASSICAL THEORY

The classical wave theory is that of the de Broglie waves for matter and of electromagnetic waves for radiation. This section will treat primarily those waves which

[1] W. Pauli, *Zeitschrift für Physik*, **31**, 765, 1925.

[2] E. Fermi, *ibid.*, **36**, 902, 1926.

[3] P. A. M. Dirac, *Proceedings of the Royal Society*, A, **112**, 661, 1926.

are associated with the electron (the proton waves can be treated in an entirely similar manner), though light waves will also be considered briefly. No attempt will be made to include relativistic effects, and it is then logical to treat only electrostatic forces and to neglect magnetic and retardational phenomena.

The proper wave equation for matter waves was first discovered by Schrödinger,[1] and is most simply obtained from the transformation equation (73) of § 5. This general Schrödinger equation (73) cannot itself be properly regarded as a true wave equation, since it is an equation in $3N$-dimensional co-ordinate space for N particles; however, for $N=1$ this space reduces to ordinary 3-space, and it is therefore reasonable to try to regard the equation in this special case as the space-time (i.e., the classical) equation for matter waves. The transformation function $\psi(xyz)$ is then to be considered as a "field scalar."

For one (corpuscular) electron the total Hamiltonian is made up of the kinetic energy $E_{\text{kin}}=(1/2\mu)(p_x^2+p_y^2+p_z^2)$ and the potential energy $E_{\text{pot}}=-eV$, where e and μ are the charge and mass of the electron respectively and V is the electrostatic potential. Hence equation (73) in this case reduces to

$$\frac{h^2}{8\pi^2\mu}\nabla^2\psi+eV\psi-\frac{h}{2\pi i}\frac{\partial\psi}{\partial t}=0 \tag{80}$$

where ∇^2 is the Laplacian operator $(\partial^2/\partial x^2)+(\partial^2/\partial y^2)+(\partial^2/\partial z^2)$. The conjugate complex equation

$$\frac{h^2}{8\pi^2\mu}\nabla^2\psi^*+eV\psi^*+\frac{h}{2\pi i}\frac{\partial\psi^*}{\partial t}=0 \tag{81}$$

is implicitly contained in equation (80).

[1] *Annalen der Physik*, **79**, 361 (1926).

The mathematical theory of these equations can be regarded as a "classical" theory of matter waves, though of course in this case the interpretation of the mathematics is essentially different from that of the foregoing sections. The quantities entering into these equations can all be visualized in terms of space and time just as can the quantities in the Maxwell equations, since they are all functions only of the four variables x, y, z, t.

The wave theory does not consider electrons, and e and μ are merely universal constants of the wave equation. Although equations (80) and (81) were obtained from the one-electron problem of the corpuscular theory, they are now in no manner restricted "to apply to one electron only," for the phrase is meaningless in the wave theory. On the contrary they have complete generality in so far as "waves of negative electricity" are concerned. From this remark it follows at once that, in contrast to the quantum theory of the one-electron problem, V no longer simply represents the potential of the external forces but also includes the potential of the matter waves themselves, that is, it takes account of the reaction of one part of the charge distribution upon another part. This theory will be as unable to represent the phenomena of atomic physics as the Maxwell theory. Its value is exclusively heuristic in that it is related to the quantum theory of waves in the same way that classical mechanics is related to the quantum theory of particles.

As a first example the case of very small wave amplitude, i.e., very low density of matter, will be treated. It will assume that the external potential is also zero, so that

V vanishes to the requisite approximation. Then equation (80) becomes

$$\frac{h^2}{8\pi^2\mu}\nabla^2\psi-\frac{h}{2\pi i}\frac{\partial\psi}{\partial t}=0\ , \tag{82}$$

which possesses the solution

$$\psi=e^{\frac{2\pi i}{h}(p_x x+p_y y+p_z z-Et)}\ ,$$

where

$$E=\frac{1}{2\mu}(p_x^2+p_y^2+p_z^2)=\frac{1}{2\mu}p^2\ .$$

These have the form of plane waves, the direction of the wave normal being given by p_x, p_y, p_z and the wave-length and frequency being

$$\lambda=\frac{h}{p}\ ,\qquad \nu=\frac{E}{h}\ . \tag{83}$$

The phase velocity v_ϕ of the waves is

$$v_\phi=\frac{E}{p}=\frac{p}{2\mu}\ , \tag{84}$$

while the group velocity v_g can be calculated from elementary optical principles to be

$$v_g=\frac{dE}{dp}=\frac{p}{\mu}=\frac{h}{\lambda\mu}\ . \tag{85}$$

According to de Broglie,[1] these are the equations which govern the interference of matter waves for very low

[1] L. de Broglie, *Annales de Physique*, 10 Série, 2, 22, 1925; *Ondes et Mouvement*, Paris, 1926.

density. The relationship between group velocity and wave-length permits an association of wave-length to moving complexes of negative electricity without in any way appealing to the particle picture. This theory of de Broglie therefore gives a simple qualitative account of the experiments of Davisson and Germer, Thomson, Rupp, and others. This is precisely analogous to the success of the classical mechanics in explaining the Wilson photographs, the deflection of cathode rays by electric fields, etc. Nevertheless one can regard these achievements of classical theories only as proof of the similarity of the classical and quantum theories, in the sense of the correspondence principle; for the answer to all quantitative questions an appeal must be made to the exact quantum theory.

Before passing on to the quantum theory of waves it will be necessary to elaborate this classical wave theory somewhat further. For this purpose we return to the wave equation (80) which is not restricted to low density of matter, and make the following assumptions for the interpretation of the wave function ψ:

$$\left.\begin{aligned} &\text{Charge density: } \rho = -e\psi^*\psi\,, \\ &\text{Current density: } \sigma = -\frac{eh}{4\pi i\mu}(\psi^*\nabla\psi - \psi\nabla\psi^*)\,, \\ &\text{Energy density: } u = \frac{h^2}{8\pi^2\mu}\nabla\psi^*\cdot\nabla\psi\,. \end{aligned}\right\} \qquad (86)$$

The strict justification of these assumptions can be found only in the later developments of the quantum theory of waves. None the less they are plausible at this point because the quantities ρ, σ, and u thus introduced obey by virtue of equations (80) and (81) the following conservation laws of the kind which must be demanded of any classical theory:

$$\text{Conservation of charge: } \frac{d}{dt}\int \rho dv = 0 \,, \tag{87a}$$

$$\text{Conservation of momentum: } \frac{d}{dt}\int \sigma dv = -e\int \nabla V \psi^* \psi dv \,, \tag{87b}$$

$$\text{Conservation of energy: } \frac{d}{dt}\int u dv = \int eV \frac{\partial}{\partial t}(\psi^*\psi) dv \,. \tag{87c}$$

In these equations dv is the volume element and the integrals are over all space. It is assumed that ψ vanishes over the infinite sphere so that whenever Green's theorem is applied the surface integral vanishes. To deduce (87a) multiply equation (80) by ψ^* and equation (81) by ψ, subtract the two equations thus obtained, integrate over all space and apply Green's theorem. To deduce (87b) multiply equation (80) by $\partial\psi^*/\partial x$, differentiate equation (81) with respect to x, multiply by ψ, and then subtract and integrate as before. Finally, (87c) is deduced in the same manner as (87a) except that the equations are added instead of subtracted.

Besides the waves of negative electricity other charges may be present in space, such as atomic nuclei, charged condensers, etc. The density of these charges will be designated by ρ_0. The total electric potential must then be determined by Poisson's equation $\nabla\cdot\mathrm{E} = 4\pi(\rho+\rho_0)$, or

$$\nabla^2 V = -4\pi(\rho+\rho_0) \,. \tag{88}$$

For the purpose of the quantum theory of wave fields to be developed in the next sections it is necessary to note that equations (80), (81), and (88) can all three be deduced from a single variation principle. The proper Lagrangian function is seen to be

$$\left.\begin{aligned} L=-\frac{h^2}{8\pi^2\mu}\nabla\psi^*\cdot\nabla\psi-\frac{h}{4\pi i}\left(\frac{\partial\psi}{\partial t}\psi^*-\frac{\partial\psi^*}{\partial t}\psi\right)& \\ +eV\psi\psi^*-\rho_0 V+\frac{1}{8\pi}\nabla V\cdot\nabla V\,,& \end{aligned}\right\}\quad(89)$$

since on varying ψ and ψ^* the condition

$$\iint L\,dv\,dt = \text{Extremum}$$

gives the equations (80) and (81), respectively, and on varying V gives equation (88).

The total energy of the system is composed of the energy of the matter waves and that of the electromagnetic field. Hence the total energy density $\mathcal{H}$ is given by the equation

$$\mathcal{H}=\frac{h^2}{8\pi^2\mu}\nabla\psi^*\cdot\nabla\psi+\frac{1}{8\pi}\nabla V\cdot\nabla V\,, \qquad (90)$$

and the conservation law

$$H=\int\mathcal{H}dv=\text{Const.} \qquad (91)$$

is readily proved, provided ρ_0 is independent of the time. The proof is as follows: From equations (90), (88), and (87c)

$$\begin{aligned} \frac{dH}{dt}&=\int dv\left[\frac{\partial u}{\partial t}-\frac{1}{4\pi}V\frac{\partial}{\partial t}(\nabla V\cdot\nabla V)\right], \\ &=\int dv\left[\frac{\partial u}{\partial t}-V\frac{\partial}{\partial t}(e\psi\psi^*)\right], \\ &=0\,. \end{aligned}$$

This self-consistent space-time theory, built according to the model of a classical field theory, does not as yet contain a single corpuscular element. This is evident above all from the fact that the total charge of the system

$$\int \rho dv = -e\int \psi^* \psi dv \tag{92}$$

can take on any desired value, and not merely the values $-e$, $-2e$, $-3e$, ... , as must be required of any true theory of atomic (or quantized) systems. Furthermore, the total energy and the characteristic frequencies can also have any value, since the differential equations are non-linear and the characteristic frequencies therefore depend on the amplitudes of ψ. In spite of these defects (which are those of any classical theory), the present theory can be used to account for atomic phenomena in a manner precisely analogous to that used by Bohr and Sommerfeld in applying the classical corpuscular theory. Just as these authors introduced the conditions $\int p_k dq_k = n_k h$ into classical mechanics, so Hartree[1] has been able to give an approximate account of atomic spectra by imposing the "quantum conditions"

$$\int \psi_k^* \psi_k dv = n_k \tag{93}$$

in the present field theory.[2] The quantity n_k is an integer, and the suffix k refers to a characteristic vibration of the system. Hartree is able to obtain satisfactory results only

[1] D. R. Hartree, *Proceedings of the Cambridge Philosophical Society*, **24**, 89, 1928.

[2] Hartree has shown that satisfactory results are obtained only if the energy of the interaction of the electron with its own field is subtracted from the total energy.

upon neglecting the periodic time-variations in V, which are produced by the periodic character of ψ. This is analogous to the difficulties encountered by the Bohr-Sommerfeld theory. It is characteristic that this field theory is quite as difficult to treat mathematically as the classical mechanics; at any rate it is far more difficult than the quantum theory of either particles or waves.

It is probably unnecessary to enter into a detailed account of the classical theory of radiation, since this is the well-known Maxwell theory. It contains no quantum element whatsoever, as witnessed by the fact that the energy $\int (\boldsymbol{E}^2+\boldsymbol{H}^2)dv$ is continuously variable. Again the difficulty may be avoided by quantum conditions like those of Hartree, which make possible only discontinuous energy changes of amount $h\nu$; this does not, however, lead to a quantum theory of the field.

§ 9. QUANTUM THEORY OF WAVE FIELDS[1]

The mathematical apparatus necessary for the quantum theory of wave fields may be put in a form completely analogous to that of the quantum mechanics of particles provided the classical wave theory is first brought into a form analogous to the Hamiltonian form of classical mechanics. The present section treats the general problem of a classical wave theory that can be derived from a variation principle. The Lagrangian function of this variation principle may contain a number of wave functions $\psi_\alpha=\psi_\alpha(x, y, z, t)$, $(\alpha=1, 2, 3, \ldots)$[e.g., ψ, ψ^*, and V of § 8], their first order space derivatives $(\partial\psi_\alpha/\partial x_i)$

[1] P. Jordan and W. Pauli, *Zeitschrift für Physik*, **47**, 151, 1928; W. Heisenberg and W. Pauli, *ibid.*, **56**, 1, 1929; **59**, 168, 1930.

($i = 1, 2, 3$ for x, y, z), and their first-order time derivatives $(\partial\psi_a/\partial t) = \dot{\psi}_a$. The variation principle will then be

$$\int\int L\left(\psi_a, \frac{\partial\psi_a}{\partial x_i}, \dot{\psi}_a\right) dv\, dt = \text{Extremum}, \qquad (94)$$

and the wave equations are the corresponding Eulerian equations

$$\frac{\partial L}{\partial\psi_a} - \sum_i \frac{\partial}{\partial x_i} \frac{\partial L}{\partial\left(\frac{\partial\psi_a}{\partial x_i}\right)} - \frac{\partial}{\partial t}\frac{\partial L}{\partial\dot{\psi}_a} = 0 \quad (a = 1, 2, \ldots). \qquad (95)$$

The classical mechanics of a system of particles may be derived entirely from Hamilton's variation principle

$$\int L(q_k, \dot{q}_k) dt = \text{Extremum}. \qquad (96)$$

The variation principle (94) for a continuous field may be made formally similar to the variation principle (96) for a discrete set of particles by introducing the quantity

$$\bar{L} = \int L\left(\psi_a, \frac{\partial\psi_a}{\partial x_i}, \dot{\psi}_a\right) dv, \qquad (97)$$

and then writing (94) in the form

$$\int \bar{L}\left(\psi_a, \frac{\partial\psi_a}{\partial x_i}, \dot{\psi}_a\right) dt = \text{Extremum}. \qquad (98)$$

Now while $L(q_k, \dot{q}_k)$ depends on the q_k for all values of the index k, $\bar{L}[\psi_a, (\partial\psi_a/\partial x_i), \dot{\psi}_a]$ is determined by the values of ψ_a and $\dot{\psi}_a$ at all points of space. Hence the analogy between the two quantities is complete *if the points P of the space be regarded as the indices of the wave function.* The complete wave function may then be regarded as the complex of quantities $\psi_a(P)$ dependent on two kinds of indices: a discrete set a and a continuously variable set P. (P, of course, takes the place of the *three* indices x, y, z.)

The Eulerian equations (95) may now be expressed in terms of the Lagrangian $\bar{L}$, which is the analogue of the Lagrangian for a system of particles. As the analogue of the ordinary derivative $(\partial/\partial q_k)L(q_i, \dot{q}_i)$, which may be written

$$\frac{\partial L}{\partial q_k} = \lim_{\Delta q = 0} \frac{L(q_i + \delta_{ik}\Delta q, \dot{q}_i) - L(q_i, \dot{q}_i)}{\Delta q},$$

we may define the derivative

$$\left.\begin{aligned}
&\frac{\delta \bar{L}\left[\psi_\beta(P'), \frac{\partial \psi_\beta(P')}{\partial x_i}, \dot{\psi}_\beta(P')\right]}{\delta \psi_a(P)} = \\
&\lim_{\Delta\psi \doteq 0} \frac{1}{\Delta\psi}\Bigg\{\bar{L}\Bigg[\psi_\beta(P') + \delta_{a\beta}\delta(P-P')\Delta\psi(P'), \\
&\qquad \frac{\partial}{\partial x_i}[\psi_\beta(P') + \delta_{a\beta}\delta(P-P')\Delta\psi(P'), \dot{\psi}_\beta(P')]\Bigg] \\
&\qquad\qquad - \bar{L}\left[\psi_\beta(P'), \frac{\partial \psi_\beta(P')}{\partial x_i}, \dot{\psi}_\beta(P')\right]\Bigg\}.
\end{aligned}\right\} \quad (99)$$

The symbol $\delta(P-P')$ stands for a function analogous to Dirac's δ-function (cf. § 2) having the properties

$$\left.\begin{aligned}
&\delta(P-P') = 0 \quad \text{when } P \neq P', \\
\text{and} \quad &\int \delta(P-P')dv = 1 \text{ or } 0,
\end{aligned}\right\} \quad (100)$$

according to whether the volume of integration contains or does not contain the point P'. From the definition (97) of $\bar{L}$ it is readily seen that

$$\frac{\delta \bar{L}}{\delta \psi_a} = \frac{\partial L}{\partial \psi_a} - \sum_i \frac{\partial}{\partial x_i} \frac{\partial L}{\partial \left(\frac{\partial \psi_a}{\partial x_i} \right)} . \tag{101}$$

Since it is obvious that

$$\frac{\delta \bar{L}}{\delta \dot{\psi}_a} = \frac{\partial L}{\partial \dot{\psi}_a} ,$$

the Eulerian equations become

$$\frac{\delta \bar{L}}{\delta \psi_a} - \frac{\partial}{\partial t} \frac{\delta \bar{L}}{\delta \dot{\psi}_a} = 0 , \tag{102}$$

in complete analogy to the Lagrangian equations of classical mechanics.

The transition from the Lagrangian to the Hamiltonian form in classical particle mechanics is brought about by introducing the Hamiltonian

$$H = \sum_k p_k \dot{q}_k - L , \tag{103}$$

where $p_k = \partial L / \partial \dot{q}_k$; the equations then take the Hamiltonian form (1). The same procedure will now be used for the wave equations (95). A conjugate Π_a to the wave function ψ_a may be introduced by the relation

$$\Pi_a = \frac{\delta \bar{L}}{\delta \dot{\psi}_a} = \frac{\partial L}{\partial \dot{\psi}_a} , \tag{104}$$

and the Hamiltonian will then be, by analogy to (103),

$$\bar{H}=\int\sum_a \Pi_a\dot{\psi}_a dv-\bar{L}\,. \tag{105}$$

Analogously to the relations between L and $\bar{L}$,

$$\bar{H}=\int H dv \tag{106}$$

if

$$H=\sum_a \Pi_a\dot{\psi}_a-L\,. \tag{107}$$

The wave equations (95) now take the Hamiltonian form

$$\dot{\psi}_a=\frac{\delta\bar{H}}{\delta\Pi_a}\,,\qquad \dot{\Pi}_a=-\frac{\delta\bar{H}}{\delta\psi_a}\,. \tag{108}$$

Conservation laws may be deduced as in particle mechanics. Directly from (108) follows the conservation of energy,

$$\frac{d\bar{H}}{dt}=0\,, \tag{109}$$

while the equations

$$\frac{d}{dt}\int\sum_a \Pi_a\frac{\partial\psi_a}{\partial x_i}dv=0\quad(i=1,\,2,\,3)\,, \tag{110}$$

expressing the conservation of momentum follow from (108) and (101), since

$$\frac{d}{dt}\int dv\sum_a \Pi_a\frac{\partial\psi_a}{\partial x_i}=\int dv\left[\Pi_a\frac{\partial}{\partial x_i}\frac{\delta\bar{H}}{\delta\Pi_a}-\frac{\partial\psi_a}{\partial x_i}\frac{\delta\bar{H}}{\delta\psi_a}\right],$$

$$=-\int dv\sum_a\left[\frac{\partial\Pi_a}{\partial x_i}\frac{\delta\bar{H}}{\delta\Pi_a}+\frac{\partial\psi_a}{\partial x_i}\frac{\delta\bar{H}}{\delta\psi_a}\right],$$

$$=-\int dv\frac{\partial H}{\partial x_i}=0\,.$$

In both cases it is assumed that H contains no function of space and time other than Π_α, ψ_α, and their derivatives.

The transition from classical theory to quantum theory can now be accomplished without difficulty by analogy to the procedure of § 1. Just as the co-ordinates were there replaced by matrices, so here the wave functions may be replaced by non-commutative variables, which can be represented as matrices in a suitably chosen Hilbert space. (Such quantities have been called "q-numbers" by Dirac.) To the differential equations (108) must then be added the exchange relations analogous to (15):

$$\left.\begin{aligned}&\Pi_\alpha(P)\psi_\beta(P')-\psi_\beta(P')\Pi_\alpha(P)=\delta_{\alpha\beta}\delta(P-P')\,\frac{h}{2\pi i}\,,\\&\Pi_\alpha(P)\Pi_\beta(P')-\Pi_\beta(P')\Pi_\alpha(P)=0\,,\\&\psi_\alpha(P)\psi_\beta(P')-\psi_\beta(P')\psi_\alpha(P)=0\,.\end{aligned}\right\}\quad(111)$$

In this quantum theory of wave fields the space-time co-ordinates x, y, z, t are thus parameters (like the time in the particle theory); they are therefore numbers in the ordinary sense (called "c-members" by Dirac), and of course commute with each other and all other quantities.

The conservation laws

$$\bar{H}=\text{Const.},\qquad \int\sum_\alpha \Pi_\alpha\,\frac{\partial\psi_\alpha}{\partial x_i}\,dv=\text{Const.}\qquad(112)$$

remain valid, as is readily proved with the help of relations (111).

The simplest method for the mathematical treatment of a wave problem defined by the equations (108) and

(111) is to develop the wave functions in a suitably chosen set of orthogonal function $u_\alpha^r(P)$:

$$\psi_\alpha = \sum_r a_r(t) u_\alpha^r(P) , \quad \Pi_\alpha = \sum_r b_r(t) u_\alpha^r(P) . \quad (113)$$

The $u_\alpha^r(P)$ are ordinary c-numbers and the coefficients a_r, b_r must then be regarded as q-numbers dependent on the time.

In order that ψ_α and Π_α when written in this form shall obey the exchange relations (111), the a_r and b_r must satisfy the exchange relations

$$\left.\begin{aligned} b_s a_r - a_r b_s &= \frac{h}{2\pi i}\,\delta_{rs} , \\ a_s a_r - a_r a_s &= 0 , \\ b_s b_r - b_r b_s &= 0 , \end{aligned}\right\} \quad (114)$$

which are formally analogous to equations (15). This is readily proved by substituting the developments (113) in equation (111), multiplying both sides by $u_\alpha^s(P) u_\beta^t(P')$, integrating over P and P' and summing over α and β. In the integration use must be made of the orthogonality relations for the u_α^r:

$$\int dv_P \sum_\alpha u_\alpha^r(P) u_\alpha^s(P) = \delta_{rs} .$$

The Hamiltonian H and the equations of motion (108) may now be expressed in terms of the a_r and b_r. The methods previously described for solution of a quantum dynamical problem are then available here—in fact, the only difference between the quantum theory of wave fields and of particles is that in the former the number of variables is infinite while in the latter it is finite.

§ 10. APPLICATION TO WAVES OF NEGATIVE CHARGE

The method of the last section will now be applied to the waves of negative charge treated in § 8. The classical Lagrangian is then

$$L=-\frac{h^2}{8\pi^2\mu}\nabla\psi^*\cdot\nabla\psi+\frac{1}{8\pi}\nabla V\cdot\nabla V+eV\psi^*\psi$$
$$-\rho_0 V-\frac{h}{4\pi i}\left(\frac{\partial\psi}{\partial t}\psi^*-\frac{\partial\psi^*}{\partial t}\psi\right).$$

Corresponding to the division of the charge density into that of the given external charges (ρ_0) and that of the internal charges (ρ) the potential V may be written $V=V_0+V_1$, where

$$\nabla^2 V_0=-4\pi\rho_0\,,\qquad \nabla^2 V_1=4\pi e\psi^*\psi\,. \qquad (115)$$

The foregoing Lagrangian may then be modified to a more convenient form by adding the total derivatives $(h/4\pi i)(\partial/\partial t)(\psi^*\psi)$ and $-(1/4\pi)\nabla\cdot(V_1\nabla V_0)$ and discarding terms involving only the known function ρ_0. This does not alter the variation problem, and in the Lagrangian

$$L=-\frac{h^2}{8\pi^2\mu}\nabla\psi^*\cdot\nabla\psi-\frac{h}{2\pi i}\frac{\partial\psi}{\partial t}\psi^*+\frac{1}{8\pi}\nabla V_1\cdot\nabla V_1$$
$$+e(V_0+V_1)\psi^*\psi \qquad (116)$$

thus obtained only ψ, ψ^*, and V_1 are to be varied.

A slight difficulty arises because of the fact that the time derivative of V_1 does not occur in (116), thus making it impossible to introduce the exchange relations (111), since the conjugate to V_1 defined by equation (104) would vanish. The dilemma is easily avoided, however, by not regarding V_1 as an independent wave function but rather treating the equation resulting from the variation of V_1 as a secondary condition. With its help V_1 may be expressed as a function of ψ and ψ^*. Since the equation obtained by varying V_1 is $\nabla^2 V_1 = 4\pi e \psi^* \psi$, V_1 is given in terms of ψ and ψ^* by the well-known solution of this equation:

$$V(P) = -e\int G(PP')\psi^*(P')\psi(P')dv_{P'} , \qquad (117)$$

where $G(PP')$ is the Green's function (in general, simply $1/r_{PP'}$) of the region in which the waves occur. On substituting this in the Lagrangian (116) the result is, after a slight modification involving again the addition of total derivatives,

$$\left.\begin{aligned} L = -\frac{h^2}{8\pi^2\mu}\nabla\psi^* \cdot \nabla\psi - \frac{h}{2\pi i}\frac{\partial\psi}{\partial t}\psi^* - eV_0\psi^*\psi \\ -\frac{e^2}{2}\int dv_{P'}\psi^*(P)\psi(P)\psi^*(P')\psi(P')G(PP') \;. \end{aligned}\right\} \qquad (118)$$

The momentum conjugate to ψ is [cf. eq. (104)]

$$\Pi = \frac{\partial L}{\partial \dot{\psi}} = -\frac{h}{2\pi i}\psi^* ,$$

and consequently the Hamiltonian is

$$H = -\frac{h}{2\pi i}\psi^* \frac{\partial\psi}{\partial t} - L ,$$

giving

$$\left.\begin{aligned}\overline{H}=&\int dv\left[\frac{h^2}{8\pi^2\mu}\nabla\psi^*\cdot\nabla\psi-eV_0\,\psi^*\psi\right]\\&+\frac{e^2}{2}\iint dv_P dv_{P'}G(PP')\psi^*(P)\psi(P)\psi^*(P')\psi(P')\,.\end{aligned}\right\}\quad(119)$$

From this classical Hamiltonian form the transition to quantum theory may be made as in § 9, by introducing the exchange relations

$$\left.\begin{aligned}&\psi(P)\psi^*(P')-\psi^*(P')\psi(P)=\delta(P-P')\,,\\&\psi(P)\psi(P')-\psi(P')\psi(P)=0\,,\\&\psi^*(P)\psi^*(P')-\psi^*(P')\psi^*(P)=0\,.\end{aligned}\right\}\quad(120)$$

The Hamiltonian may again be taken over from the expression (119) of the classical theory. However, the order of factors, which is now of importance, is not determined in this way; in fact, the correct form, in so far as it involves the order of factors, can only be determined empirically. It has been found by Jordan and Klein[1] that the proper Hamiltonian for matter waves is

$$\left.\begin{aligned}\overline{H}=&\int dv\left[\frac{h^2}{8\pi^2\mu}\nabla\psi^*\cdot\nabla\psi-eV_0\,\psi^*\psi\right]\\&+\frac{e^2}{2}\iint dv_P dv_{P'}G(PP')\psi^*(P)\psi^*(P')\psi(P)\psi(P')\,.\end{aligned}\right\}\quad(121)$$

It should be remarked that the definition of ψ^* as the conjugate of ψ requires some modification when ψ is a q-number. If ψ is given as a function of Hermitian ma-

[1] P. Jordan and O. Klein, *Zeitschrift für Physik*, 45, 751, 1927.

trices, then ψ^* is obtained from it by replacing i by $-i$ and also interchanging the order of factors, e.g.,

$$(pq)^* = q^* p^* .$$

In this quantum theory of matter waves the total charge

$$-e\int dv\psi^*\psi$$

is again a constant in time, as is most readily proved by showing that it commutes with $\overline{\overline{H}}$. As must also be the case, its characteristic values are integral multiples of $-e$. This may be shown in the following manner. As in § 9, if we put

$$\left.\begin{aligned} \psi = \sum_r a_r u_r(P) \, , \qquad \psi^* = \sum_r a_r^* u_r(P) \, , \\ \int u_r u_s \, dv = \delta_{rs} \, , \end{aligned}\right\} \qquad (122)$$

the a_r and a_r^* satisfy the exchange relations

$$\left.\begin{aligned} a_r a_s^* - a_s^* a_r = \delta_{rs} \, , \\ a_r a_s - a_s a_r = 0 \, , \\ a_r^* a_s^* - a_s^* a_r^* = 0 \, , \end{aligned}\right\} \qquad (123)$$

analogous to equations (114). The foregoing exchange relations may be satisfied by setting

$$a_r = e^{-\frac{2\pi i}{h}\Theta_r} N_r^{\frac{1}{2}} \, , \qquad a_r^* = N_r^{\frac{1}{2}} e^{\frac{2\pi i}{h}\Theta_r} \, , \qquad (124)$$

provided N_r and Θ_r are Hermitian operators satisfying the exchange relations

$$\Theta_r N_s - N_s \Theta_r = \delta_{rs} \, .$$

It is then possible to prove that

$$e^{-\frac{2\pi i}{h}\Theta_r} f(N_r) = f(N_r+1) e^{-\frac{2\pi i}{h}\Theta_r} , \qquad (125)$$

and that the characteristic values of the N_r are positive integers. It then follows from equation (122) that

$$e\int dv\psi^*\psi = e\int dv \sum_{r,s} a_r^* a_s u_r u_s$$
$$= e\sum_{r,s} a_r^* a_s = e\sum_r N_r .$$

The quantum theory of matter waves thus accounts for the existence of the electron. At the same time it is evident that the Hartree "quantum conditions" 93) are the analogue, in the sense of the correspondence principle, of the exchange relations (123). Since ΣN_r is a constant of integration of the equations of motion it is possible to consider separately those stationary states for which this quantity has the numerical value N. (It may be remarked that ΣN_r is a constant even when V_0 depends on the time.) It has been shown by Jordan and Klein (cf. § 11)[1] that the solutions of the wave problem with Hamiltonian (119) for which this condition is fulfilled are mathematically and physically equivalent to the solutions of the N-electron problem of the corpuscular theory, i.e., to the solutions of the Schrödinger equation (47). However, they do not correspond to all the solutions of this equation but only to those of the possible solutions in which the transformation function ψ is symmetric in the

[1] *Ibid.*

co-ordinates of the electrons. These solutions themselves form a closed term system, namely, that one for which the Bose-Einstein statistics is valid. The quantum theory of matter waves [especially the exchange relations (111)] thus requires the Bose-Einstein statistics for the corresponding particle picture.

The exchange relations (111) are, however, only one possibility out of many. Another equally justifiable set is obtained by changing the minus sign into a plus sign, so that the wave functions satisfy the equations

$$\left.\begin{array}{l}\psi(P)\psi^*(P')+\psi^*(P')\psi(P)=\delta(P-P')\ , \\ \psi(P)\psi(P')+\psi(P')\psi(P)=0\ , \\ \psi^*(P)\psi^*(P')+\psi^*(P')\psi^*(P)=0\ .\end{array}\right\} \qquad (126)$$

According to Jordan and Wigner,[1] the quantum theory of waves based on these exchange relations is equivalent to the antisymmetric solutions of the Schrödinger equation; that is, these relations lead to the Pauli exclusion principle and the corresponding Fermi-Dirac statistics.

§ 11. PROOF OF THE MATHEMATICAL EQUIVALENCE OF THE QUANTUM THEORY OF PARTICLES AND OF WAVES

The problem of quantum theory centers on the fact that the particle picture and the wave picture are merely two different aspects of one and the same physical reality. Although this is a problem of purely physical nature it is satisfying to find a counterpart to this duality in the

[1] P. Jordan and E. Wigner, *Zeitschrift für Physik*, **47**, 631, 1928.

mathematical apparatus of the theory. The analogy consists in the fact that one and the same set of mathematical equations can be interpreted at will in terms of either picture.

The proof of this assertion may be made perfectly general without regard to the particular form of Hamiltonian considered. The Schrödinger equation of the particle picture for N equivalent particles may be written

$$\left\{\sum_{n=1}^{N} O^n + \sum_{n>m}^{N} O^{nm} + \cdot \cdot + \frac{h}{2\pi i}\frac{\partial}{\partial t}\right\}\varphi(\boldsymbol{x}_1, \ldots, \boldsymbol{x}_N) = 0 \quad (127)$$

where O^n is an operator acting only on the space co-ordinates $\boldsymbol{x}_n$ of the nth particle, and O^{nm} one acting on the co-ordinates of both the nth and mth. Furthermore, it may be assumed that a certain system of orthogonal functions $u_r(\boldsymbol{x})$ has been found, in terms of which all functions in 3-space satisfying the boundary conditions can be expanded; it will then be possible to expand $\varphi(\boldsymbol{x}_1, \ldots, \boldsymbol{x}_N)$ in terms of products of these functions:

$$\varphi(\boldsymbol{x}_1, \ldots, \boldsymbol{x}_N) = \sum_{r_1 \ldots r_N} b(r_1, \ldots, r_N, t) u_{r_1}(\boldsymbol{x}_1) \ldots u_{r_N}(\boldsymbol{x}_N) \,. \quad (128)$$

The quantities $|b(r_1 \ldots r_N, t)|^2$ may be regarded as determining the probability that the particle 1 is in the r_1-state, particle 2 in the r_2-state, etc. If this expression for φ be substituted in equation (127), the result multiplied by $u_{s_1}(\boldsymbol{x}_1) u_{s_2}(\boldsymbol{x}_2) \ldots u_{s_N}(\boldsymbol{x}_N)$ and then integrated over

$x_1, x_2, \ldots, x_N$ there results the following differential equation for the b's:

$$\left.\begin{aligned} 0 = {} & \frac{h}{2\pi i}\frac{\partial}{\partial t} b(s_1, s_2, \ldots, s_N, t) \\ & + \sum_n \sum_{r_m} O^n_{s_n r_m} b\,(s_1 \ldots r_m \ldots s_N) \\ & + \sum_{n>m} \sum_{r_n r_m} O^{nm}_{s_n s_m;\, r_n r_m} b(s_1 \ldots r_n \ldots r_m \ldots s_N) + \cdots \end{aligned}\right\} \quad (129)$$

Use has here been made of the orthogonality relations for the $u_r(x)$ and the quantities

$$O^n_{s_n r_n} = \int u_{s_n} O^n u_{r_n} dv_n \ ,$$

$$O^{nm}_{s_n s_m;\, r_n r_m} = \int\int u_{s_n} u_{s_m} O^{nm} u_{r_n} u_{r_m} dv_n dv_m \ ,$$

are the elements of the matrices representing the corresponding operators in the co-ordinate system characterized by the functions $u_r(x)$. Because of the symmetry of the Hamiltonian in the co-ordinates of the particles, the numerical values of the matrix elements depend only on the indices r and s, and not explicitly on n and m. In the case of the Bose-Einstein statistics the $b(s_1 \ldots s_N)$ are symmetric in the quantum numbers of the particles, so that they can also be expressed as functions of the number N_r of particles in the rth state. Since the a priori probability of finding N_1 particles in the first state, N_2 in the second, etc., is then given by $Z^2 = N!/(N_1!\,N_2! \ldots)$, it is convenient to define the quantity

$$b(N_1, N_2 \ldots) = Zb(r_1, r_2, \ldots, r_N). \qquad (130)$$

The operators $e^{-\frac{2\pi i}{h}\Theta_r}$ of equation (125) which change N_r to N_r+1 are useful here; with their aid equation (129) may be written

$$0=\left\{\frac{h}{2\pi i}\frac{\partial}{\partial t}+\sum_{s,r}N_s O_{sr}e^{\frac{2\pi i}{h}(\Theta_s-\Theta_r)}\right.$$
$$+\frac{1}{2}\sum_{ss';rr'}N_s(N_{s'}-\delta_{ss'})O_{ss';rr'}e^{\frac{2\pi i}{h}(\Theta_s+\Theta_{s'}-\Theta_r-\Theta_{r'})}$$
$$\left.+\ldots\right\}\frac{1}{Z}b(N_1, N_2, \ldots).$$

On multiplying this equation from the left by Z and commuting $1/Z$ to the left equation (125) yields

$$\left.\begin{aligned}0=&\left\{\frac{h}{2\pi i}\frac{\partial}{\partial t}+\sum_{s,r}N_s^{\frac{1}{2}}(N_s-\delta_{rs}+1)^{\frac{1}{2}}O_{sr}e^{\frac{2\pi i}{h}(\Theta_s-\Theta_r)}\right.\\&+\frac{1}{2}\sum_{ss';rr'}N_s^{\frac{1}{2}}(N_{s'}-\delta_{ss'})^{\frac{1}{2}}(N_r+1-\delta_{rs}-\delta_{rs'})^{\frac{1}{2}}\\&\left.(N_{r'}+1+\delta_{rr'}-\delta_{r's}-\delta_{r's'})^{\frac{1}{2}}\cdot e^{\frac{2\pi i}{h}(\Theta_s+\Theta_{s'}-\Theta_r-\Theta_{r'})}\right\}\\&\cdot b(N_1, N_2, \ldots).\end{aligned}\right\}\quad(131)$$

We turn now to the corresponding problem expressed in the wave theory; the Hamiltonian corresponding to (127) is then

$$\bar{H}=\int dv_P\psi_P^*O^P\psi_{P'}+\frac{1}{2}\int\int dv_P dv_{P'}\psi_{P'}^*\psi_P^*O^{P'P}\psi_{P'}\psi_P+\ldots.$$

By (122) this may also be written

$$\bar{H}=\sum_{s,r}a_s^*a_rO_{sr}+\frac{1}{2}\sum_{ss';rr'}a_s^*a_{s'}^*a_ra_{r'}O_{ss';rr'}+\ldots.$$

Then on substituting equations (124) in the equation

$$\bar{H}S+\frac{h}{2\pi i}\frac{\partial S}{\partial t}=0\ ,$$

we obtain

$$0=\left\{\frac{h}{2\pi i}\frac{\partial}{\partial t}+\sum_{s,r}N_s^{\frac{1}{2}}O_{sr}e^{\frac{2\pi i}{h}(\Theta_s-\Theta_r)}N_r^{\frac{1}{2}}\right.$$

$$+\tfrac{1}{2}\sum_{ss';\,rr'}N_s^{\frac{1}{2}}e^{\frac{2\pi i}{h}\Theta_{s'}}O_{ss';\,rr'}e^{\frac{2\pi i}{h}\Theta_r}N_r^{\frac{1}{2}}e^{-\frac{2\pi i}{h}\Theta_{r'}}N_{r'}^{\frac{1}{2}}$$

$$\left.+\ \cdots\cdot\right\}S(N_1,N_2,\ldots\ldots)\ .$$

Commutation of the operators $e^{\frac{2\pi i}{h}\Theta}$ to the right gives

$$\left.\begin{aligned}0=\Big\{&\frac{h}{2\pi i}\frac{\partial}{\partial t}+N_s^{\frac{1}{2}}(N_r-\delta_{sr}+1)^{\frac{1}{2}}O_{sr}e^{\frac{2\pi i}{h}(\Theta_s-\Theta_r)}\\&+\tfrac{1}{2}\sum_{ss';\,rr'}N_s^{\frac{1}{2}}(N_{s'}-\delta_{ss'})^{\frac{1}{2}}(N_r+1-\delta_{rs'}-\delta_{rs})^{\frac{1}{2}}\\&(N_{r'}+1+\delta_{rr'}-\delta_{r's}-\delta_{r's'})^{\frac{1}{2}}e^{\frac{2\pi i}{h}(\Theta_s+\Theta_{s'}-\Theta_r-\Theta_{r'})}\Big\}S\ .\end{aligned}\right\}\quad(132)$$

This equation is identical with equation (131), and the mathematical equivalence of the particle and wave pictures has therefore been proved. A similar proof may be given in the case of the Pauli exclusion principle and the exchange relations (126).

Although the classical theories of the corpuscular and wave pictures are so entirely different, both physically and mathematically, the quantum theories of the two are identical.

§ 12. APPLICATION TO THE THEORY OF RADIATION[1]

It will be recalled that the Maxwell equations, which govern the classical wave theory of radiation, can be derived by variation of the potentials in the Lagrangian

$$L=\frac{1}{8\pi}(\boldsymbol{E}^2-\boldsymbol{H}^2)+\sum_{\alpha=1}^{4}\Phi_\alpha s_\alpha .$$

The $s_\alpha(\alpha=1, 2, 3, 4)$ are the components of the 4-current density, the Φ_α the 4-potentials ($\Phi_4=i\Phi_0$, $x_4=ict$); hence the Lagrangian becomes, when written explicitly in terms of the potentials,

$$\left.\begin{aligned}L=\frac{1}{8\pi}\left[\sum_i\left(\frac{1}{c}\frac{\partial\Phi_i}{\partial t}+\frac{\partial\Phi_0}{\partial x_i}\right)^2-\sum_{i>k}\left(\frac{\partial\Phi_i}{\partial x_k}-\frac{\partial\Phi_k}{\partial x_i}\right)^2\right]\\+\sum_\alpha\Phi_\alpha s_\alpha .\end{aligned}\right\}\quad(133)$$

(In this and the following equations Latin indices run from 1 to 3, Greek indices from 1 to 4.)

The momentum conjugate to Φ_i is, by (104),

$$\Pi_i=\frac{\partial L}{\partial\dot{\Phi}_i}=\frac{1}{4\pi c}\left(\frac{1}{c}\frac{\partial\Phi_i}{\partial t}+\frac{\partial\Phi_0}{\partial x_i}\right)=\frac{1}{4\pi c}E_i . \qquad (134)$$

Since the Bose-Einstein statistics applies to light quanta, the proper exchange relations are

$$E_i(P)\Phi_\alpha(P')-\Phi_\alpha(P')E_i(P)=-2hci\,\delta(P-P')\delta_{i\alpha} ,$$

[1] W. Heisenberg and W. Pauli, *Zeitschrift für Physik*, **56**, 1, 1929.

which give on differentiating

$$\left.\begin{aligned} &E_i(P)E_k(P')-E_k(P')E_i(P)=0\ ,\\ &H_i(P)H_k(P')-H_k(P')H_i(P)=0\ ,\\ &E_i(P)H_k(P')-H_k(P')H_i(P)=-2hci\,\frac{\partial\delta(P-P')}{\partial x_j}\ , \end{aligned}\right\}\quad(135)$$

where i, j, k is any cyclic permutation of 1, 2, 3.

A difficulty arises from the circumstance that $\dot{\Phi}_0$ does not occur in the Lagrangian; this affects, however, only the exchange relations between potentials and field components, and not the exchange relations (135).

If the Φ_a be developed in a set of suitably chosen orthogonal functions (e.g., standing waves in an inclosure), then the energy content of a vibration of frequency ν becomes an integral multiple of $h\nu$. Dirac[1] has shown that this makes it possible to consider the number of light quanta in each state as the variables of the system; this constitutes the link with the particle picture.

[1] *Proceedings of the Royal Society*, A, **114**, 710, 1927.

INDEX

CATALOGUE OF DOVER BOOKS

BOOKS EXPLAINING SCIENCE AND MATHEMATICS

General

WHAT IS SCIENCE?, Norman Campbell. This excellent introduction explains scientific method, role of mathematics, types of scientific laws. Contents: 2 aspects of science, science & nature, laws of science, discovery of laws, explanation of laws, measurement & numerical laws, applications of science. 192pp. 5⅜ x 8. S43 Paperbound **$1.25**

THE COMMON SENSE OF THE EXACT SCIENCES, W. K. Clifford. Introduction by James Newman, edited by Karl Pearson. For 70 years this has been a guide to classical scientific and mathematical thought. Explains with unusual clarity basic concepts, such as extension of meaning of symbols, characteristics of surface boundaries, properties of plane figures, vectors, Cartesian method of determining position, etc. Long preface by Bertrand Russell. Bibliography of Clifford. Corrected, 130 diagrams redrawn. 249pp. 5⅜ x 8. T61 Paperbound **$1.60**

SCIENCE THEORY AND MAN, Erwin Schrödinger. This is a complete and unabridged reissue of SCIENCE AND THE HUMAN TEMPERAMENT plus an additional essay: "What is an Elementary Particle?" Nobel laureate Schrödinger discusses such topics as nature of scientific method, the nature of science, chance and determinism, science and society, conceptual models for physical entities, elementary particles and wave mechanics. Presentation is popular and may be followed by most people with little or no scientific training. "Fine practical preparation for a time when laws of nature, human institutions . . . are undergoing a critical examination without parallel," Waldemar Kaempffert, N. Y. TIMES. 192pp. 5⅜ x 8. T428 Paperbound **$1.35**

FADS AND FALLACIES IN THE NAME OF SCIENCE, Martin Gardner. Examines various cults, quack systems, frauds, delusions which at various times have masqueraded as science. Accounts of hollow-earth fanatics like Symmes; Velikovsky and wandering planets; Hoerbiger; Bellamy and the theory of multiple moons; Charles Fort; dowsing, pseudoscientific methods for finding water, ores, oil. Sections on naturopathy, iridiagnosis, zone therapy, food fads, etc. Analytical accounts of Wilhelm Reich and orgone sex energy; L. Ron Hubbard and Dianetics; A. Korzybski and General Semantics; many others. Brought up to date to include Bridey Murphy, others. Not just a collection of anecdotes, but a fair, reasoned appraisal of eccentric theory. Formerly titled IN THE NAME OF SCIENCE. Preface. Index. x + 384pp. 5⅜ x 8. T394 Paperbound **$1.50**

A DOVER SCIENCE SAMPLER, edited by George Barkin. 64-page book, sturdily bound, containing excerpts from over 20 Dover books, explaining science. Edwin Hubble, George Sarton, Ernst Mach, A. d'Abro, Galileo, Newton, others, discussing island universes, scientific truth, biological phenomena, stability in bridges, etc. Copies limited; no more than 1 to a customer, FREE

POPULAR SCIENTIFIC LECTURES, Hermann von Helmholtz. Helmholtz was a superb expositor as well as a scientist of genius in many areas. The seven essays in this volume are models of clarity, and even today they rank among the best general descriptions of their subjects ever written. "The Physiological Causes of Harmony in Music" was the first significant physiological explanation of musical consonance and dissonance. Two essays, "On the Interaction of Natural Forces" and "On the Conservation of Force," were of great importance in the history of science, for they firmly established the principle of the conservation of energy. Other lectures include "On the Relation of Optics to Painting," "On Recent Progress in the Theory of Vision," "On Goethe's Scientific Researches," and "On the Origin and Significance of Geometrical Axioms." Selected and edited with an introduction by Professor Morris Kline. xii + 286pp. 5⅜ x 8½. T799 Paperbound **$1.45**

BOOKS EXPLAINING SCIENCE AND MATHEMATICS

Physics

CONCERNING THE NATURE OF THINGS, Sir William Bragg. Christmas lectures delivered at the Royal Society by Nobel laureate. Why a spinning ball travels in a curved track; how uranium is transmuted to lead, etc. Partial contents: atoms, gases, liquids, crystals, metals, etc. No scientific background needed; wonderful for intelligent child. 32pp. of photos, 57 figures. xii + 232pp. 5⅜ x 8. T31 Paperbound **$1.50**

THE RESTLESS UNIVERSE, Max Born. New enlarged version of this remarkably readable account by a Nobel laureate. Moving from sub-atomic particles to universe, the author explains in very simple terms the latest theories of wave mechanics. Partial contents: air and its relatives, electrons & ions, waves & particles, electronic structure of the atom, nuclear physics. Nearly 1000 illustrations, including 7 animated sequences. 325pp. 6 x 9. T412 Paperbound **$2.00**

FROM EUCLID TO EDDINGTON: A STUDY OF THE CONCEPTIONS OF THE EXTERNAL WORLD, Sir Edmund Whittaker. A foremost British scientist traces the development of theories of natural philosophy from the western rediscovery of Euclid to Eddington, Einstein, Dirac, etc. The inadequacy of classical physics is contrasted with present day attempts to understand the physical world through relativity, non-Euclidean geometry, space curvature, wave mechanics, etc. 5 major divisions of examination: Space; Time and Movement; the Concepts of Classical Physics; the Concepts of Quantum Mechanics; the Eddington Universe. 212pp. 5⅜ x 8.
T491 Paperbound **$1.35**

PHYSICS, THE PIONEER SCIENCE, L. W. Taylor. First thorough text to place all important physical phenomena in cultural-historical framework; remains best work of its kind. Exposition of physical laws, theories developed chronologically, with great historical, illustrative experiments diagrammed, described, worked out mathematically. Excellent physics text for self-study as well as class work. Vol. 1: Heat, Sound: motion, acceleration, gravitation, conservation of energy, heat engines, rotation, heat, mechanical energy, etc. 211 illus. 407pp. 5⅜ x 8. Vol. 2: Light, Electricity: images, lenses, prisms, magnetism, Ohm's law, dynamos, telegraph, quantum theory, decline of mechanical view of nature, etc. Bibliography. 13 table appendix. Index. 551 illus. 2 color plates. 508pp. 5⅜ x 8.
Vol. 1 S565 Paperbound **$2.00**
Vol. 2 S566 Paperbound **$2.00**
The set **$4.00**

A SURVEY OF PHYSICAL THEORY, Max Planck. One of the greatest scientists of all time, creator of the quantum revolution in physics, writes in non-technical terms of his own discoveries and those of other outstanding creators of modern physics. Planck wrote this book when science had just crossed the threshold of the new physics, and he communicates the excitement felt then as he discusses electromagnetic theories, statistical methods, evolution of the concept of light, a step-by-step description of how he developed his own momentous theory, and many more of the basic ideas behind modern physics. Formerly "A Survey of Physics." Bibliography. Index. 128pp. 5⅜ x 8.
S650 Paperbound **$1.15**

THE ATOMIC NUCLEUS, M. Korsunsky. The only non-technical comprehensive account of the atomic nucleus in English. For college physics students, etc. Chapters cover: Radioactivity, the Nuclear Model of the Atom, the Mass of Atomic Nuclei, the Disintegration of Atomic Nuclei, the Discovery of the Positron, the Artificial Transformation of Atomic Nuclei, Artificial Radioactivity, Mesons, the Neutrino, the Structure of Atomic Nuclei and Forces Acting Between Nuclear Particles, Nuclear Fission, Chain Reaction, Peaceful Uses, Thermoculear Reactions. Slightly abridged edition. Translated by G. Yankovsky. 65 figures. Appendix includes 45 photographic illustrations. 413 pp. 5⅜ x 8.
S1052 Paperbound **$2.00**

PRINCIPLES OF MECHANICS SIMPLY EXPLAINED, Morton Mott-Smith. Excellent, highly readable introduction to the theories and discoveries of classical physics. Ideal for the layman who desires a foundation which will enable him to understand and appreciate contemporary developments in the physical sciences. Discusses: Density, The Law of Gravitation, Mass and Weight, Action and Reaction, Kinetic and Potential Energy, The Law of Inertia, Effects of Acceleration, The Independence of Motions, Galileo and the New Science of Dynamics, Newton and the New Cosmos, The Conservation of Momentum, and other topics. Revised edition of "This Mechanical World." Illustrated by E. Kosa, Jr. Bibliography and Chronology. Index. xiv + 171pp. 5⅜ x 8½.
T1067 Paperbound **$1.00**

THE CONCEPT OF ENERGY SIMPLY EXPLAINED, Morton Mott-Smith. Elementary, non-technical exposition which traces the story of man's conquest of energy, with particular emphasis on the developments during the nineteenth century and the first three decades of our own century. Discusses man's earlier efforts to harness energy, more recent experiments and discoveries relating to the steam engine, the engine indicator, the motive power of heat, the principle of excluded perpetual motion, the bases of the conservation of energy, the concept of entropy, the internal combustion engine, mechanical refrigeration, and many other related topics. Also much biographical material. Index. Bibliography. 33 illustrations. ix + 215pp. 5⅜ x 8½.
T1071 Paperbound **$1.25**

HEAT AND ITS WORKINGS, Morton Mott-Smith. One of the best elementary introductions to the theory and attributes of heat, covering such matters as the laws governing the effect of heat on solids, liquids and gases, the methods by which heat is measured, the conversion of a substance from one form to another through heating and cooling, evaporation, the effects of pressure on boiling and freezing points, and the three ways in which heat is transmitted (conduction, convection, radiation). Also brief notes on major experiments and discoveries. Concise, but complete, it presents all the essential facts about the subject in readable style. Will give the layman and beginning student a first-rate background in this major topic in physics. Index. Bibliography. 50 illustrations. x + 165pp. 5⅜ x 8½. T978 Paperbound **$1.00**

THE STORY OF ATOMIC THEORY AND ATOMIC ENERGY, J. G. Feinberg. Wider range of facts on physical theory, cultural implications, than any other similar source. Completely non-technical. Begins with first atomic theory, 600 B.C., goes through A-bomb, developments to 1959. Avogadro, Rutherford, Bohr, Einstein, radioactive decay, binding energy, radiation danger, future benefits of nuclear power, dozens of other topics, told in lively, related, informal manner. Particular stress on European atomic research. "Deserves special mention . . . authoritative," Saturday Review. Formerly "The Atom Story." New chapter to 1959. Index. 34 illustrations. 251pp. 5⅜ x 8.
T625 Paperbound **$1.60**

THE STRANGE STORY OF THE QUANTUM, AN ACCOUNT FOR THE GENERAL READER OF THE GROWTH OF IDEAS UNDERLYING OUR PRESENT ATOMIC KNOWLEDGE, B. Hoffmann. Presents lucidly and expertly, with barest amount of mathematics, the problems and theories which led to modern quantum physics. Dr. Hoffmann begins with the closing years of the 19th century, when certain trifling discrepancies were noticed, and with illuminating analogies and examples takes you through the brilliant concepts of Planck, Einstein, Pauli, de Broglie, Bohr, Schroedinger, Heisenberg, Dirac, Sommerfeld, Feynman, etc. This edition includes a new, long postscript carrying the story through 1958. "Of the books attempting an account of the history and contents of our modern atomic physics which have come to my attention, this is the best," H. Margenau, Yale University, in "American Journal of Physics." 32 tables and line illustrations. Index. 275pp. 5⅜ x 8. T518 Paperbound **$1.50**

THE EVOLUTION OF SCIENTIFIC THOUGHT FROM NEWTON TO EINSTEIN, A. d'Abro. Einstein's special and general theories of relativity, with their historical implications, are analyzed in non-technical terms. Excellent accounts of the contributions of Newton, Riemann, Weyl, Planck, Eddington, Maxwell, Lorentz and others are treated in terms of space and time, equations of electromagnetics, finiteness of the universe, methodology of science. 21 diagrams. 482pp. 5⅜ x 8. T2 Paperound **$2.25**

THE RISE OF THE NEW PHYSICS, A. d'Abro. A half-million word exposition, formerly titled THE DECLINE OF MECHANISM, for readers not versed in higher mathematics. The only thorough explanation, in everyday language, of the central core of modern mathematical physical theory, treating both classical and modern theoretical physics, and presenting in terms almost anyone can understand the equivalent of 5 years of study of mathematical physics. Scientifically impeccable coverage of mathematical-physical thought from the Newtonian system up through the electronic theories of Dirac and Heisenberg and Fermi's statistics. Combines both history and exposition; provides a broad yet unified and detailed view, with constant comparison of classical and modern views on phenomena and theories. "A must for anyone doing serious study in the physical sciences," JOURNAL OF THE FRANKLIN INSTITUTE. "Extraordinary faculty . . . to explain ideas and theories of theoretical physics in the language of daily life," ISIS. First part of set covers philosophy of science, drawing upon the practice of Newton, Maxwell, Poincaré, Einstein, others, discussing modes of thought, experiment, interpretations of causality, etc. In the second part, 100 pages explain grammar and vocabulary of mathematics, with discussions of functions, groups, series, Fourier series, etc. The remainder is devoted to concrete, detailed coverage of both classical and quantum physics, explaining such topics as analytic mechanics, Hamilton's principle, wave theory of light, electromagnetic waves, groups of transformations, thermodynamics, phase rule, Brownian movement, kinetics, special relativity, Planck's original quantum theory, Bohr's atom, Zeeman effect, Broglie's wave mechanics, Heisenberg's uncertainty, Eigen-values, matrices, scores of other important topics. Discoveries and theories are covered for such men as Alembert, Born, Cantor, Debye, Euler, Foucault, Galois, Gauss, Hadamard, Kelvin, Kepler, Laplace, Maxwell, Pauli, Rayleigh, Volterra, Weyl, Young, more than 180 others. Indexed. 97 illustrations. ix + 982pp. 5⅜ x 8.
T3 Volume 1, Paperbound **$2.00**
T4 Volume 2, Paperbound **$2.00**

SPINNING TOPS AND GYROSCOPIC MOTION, John Perry. Well-known classic of science still unsurpassed for lucid, accurate, delightful exposition. How quasi-rigidity is induced in flexible and fluid bodies by rapid motions; why gyrostat falls, top rises; nature and effect on climatic conditions of earth's precessional movement; effect of internal fluidity on rotating bodies, etc. Appendixes describe practical uses to which gyroscopes have been put in ships, compasses, monorail transportation. 62 figures. 128pp. 5⅜ x 8. T416 Paperbound **$1.00**

THE UNIVERSE OF LIGHT, Sir William Bragg. No scientific training needed to read Nobel Prize winner's expansion of his Royal Institute Christmas Lectures. Insight into nature of light, methods and philosophy of science. Explains lenses, reflection, color, resonance, polarization, x-rays, the spectrum, Newton's work with prisms, Huygens' with polarization, Crookes' with cathode ray, etc. Leads into clear statement of 2 major historical theories of light, corpuscle and wave. Dozens of experiments you can do. 199 illus., including 2 full-page color plates. 293pp. 5⅜ x 8. S538 Paperbound **$1.85**

THE STORY OF X-RAYS FROM RÖNTGEN TO ISOTOPES, A. R. Bleich. Non-technical history of x-rays, their scientific explanation, their applications in medicine, industry, research, and art, and their effect on the individual and his descendants. Includes amusing early reactions to Röntgen's discovery, cancer therapy, detections of art and stamp forgeries, potential risks to patient and operator, etc. Illustrations show x-rays of flower structure, the gall bladder, gears with hidden defects, etc. Original Dover publication. Glossary. Bibliography. Index. 55 photos and figures. xiv + 186pp. 5⅜ x 8. T662 Paperbound **$1.35**

ELECTRONS, ATOMS, METALS AND ALLOYS, Wm. Hume-Rothery. An introductory-level explanation of the application of the electronic theory to the structure and properties of metals and alloys, taking into account the new theoretical work done by mathematical physicists. Material presented in dialogue-form between an "Old Metallurgist" and a "Young Scientist." Their discussion falls into 4 main parts: the nature of an atom, the nature of a metal, the nature of an alloy, and the structure of the nucleus. They cover such topics as the hydrogen atom, electron waves, wave mechanics, Brillouin zones, co-valent bonds, radioactivity and natural disintegration, fundamental particles, structure and fission of the nucleus,etc. Revised, enlarged edition. 177 illustrations. Subject and name indexes. 407pp. 5⅜ x 8½. S1046 Paperbound **$2.25**

OUT OF THE SKY, H. H. Nininger. A non-technical but comprehensive introduction to "meteoritics", the young science concerned with all aspects of the arrival of matter from outer space. Written by one of the world's experts on meteorites, this work shows how, despite difficulties of observation and sparseness of data, a considerable body of knowledge has arisen. It defines meteors and meteorites; studies fireball clusters and processions, meteorite composition, size, distribution, showers, explosions, origins, craters, and much more. A true connecting link between astronomy and geology. More than 175 photos, 22 other illustrations. References. Bibliography of author's publications on meteorites. Index. viii + 336pp. 5⅜ x 8.
T519 Paperbound **$1.85**

SATELLITES AND SCIENTIFIC RESEARCH, D. King-Hele. Non-technical account of the manmade satellites and the discoveries they have yielded up to the autumn of 1961. Brings together information hitherto published only in hard-to-get scientific journals. Includes the life history of a typical satellite, methods of tracking, new information on the shape of the earth, zones of radiation, etc. Over 60 diagrams and 6 photographs. Mathematical appendix. Bibliography of over 100 items. Index. xii + 180pp. 5⅜ x 8½.
T703 Paperbound **$2.00**

BOOKS EXPLAINING SCIENCE AND MATHEMATICS

Mathematics

CHANCE, LUCK AND STATISTICS: THE SCIENCE OF CHANCE, Horace C. Levinson. Theory of probability and science of statistics in simple, non-technical language. Part I deals with theory of probability, covering odd superstitions in regard to "luck," the meaning of betting odds, the law of mathematical expectation, gambling, and applications in poker, roulette, lotteries, dice, bridge, and other games of chance. Part II discusses the misuse of statistics, the concept of statistical probabilities, normal and skew frequency distributions, and statistics applied to various fields—birth rates, stock speculation, insurance rates, advertising, etc. "Presented in an easy humorous style which I consider the best kind of expository writing," Prof. A. C. Cohen, Industry Quality Control. Enlarged revised edition. Formerly titled "The Science of Chance." Preface and two new appendices by the author. Index. xiv + 365pp. 5⅜ x 8.
T1007 Paperbound **$1.85**

PROBABILITIES AND LIFE, Emile Borel. Translated by M. Baudin. Non-technical, highly readable introduction to the results of probability as applied to everyday situations. Partial contents: Fallacies About Probabilities Concerning Life After Death; Negligible Probabilities and the Probabilities of Everyday Life; Events of Small Probability; Application of Probabilities to Certain Problems of Heredity; Probabilities of Deaths, Diseases, and Accidents; On Poisson's Formula. Index. 3 Appendices of statistical studies and tables. vi + 87pp. 5⅜ x 8½.
T121 Paperbound **$1.00**

GREAT IDEAS OF MODERN MATHEMATICS: THEIR NATURE AND USE, Jagjit Singh. Reader with only high school math will understand main mathematical ideas of modern physics, astronomy, genetics, psychology, evolution, etc., better than many who use them as tools, but comprehend little of their basic structure. Author uses his wide knowledge of non-mathematical fields in brilliant exposition of differential equations, matrices, group theory, logic, statistics, problems of mathematical foundations, imaginary numbers, vectors, etc. Original publication. 2 appendices. 2 indexes. 65 illustr. 322pp. 5⅜ x 8. S587 Paperbound **$1.75**

MATHEMATICS IN ACTION, O. G. Sutton. Everyone with a command of high school algebra will find this book one of the finest possible introductions to the application of mathematics to physical theory. Ballistics, numerical analysis, waves and wavelike phenomena, Fourier series, group concepts, fluid flow and aerodynamics, statistical measures, and meteorology are discussed with unusual clarity. Some calculus and differential equations theory is developed by the author for the reader's help in the more difficult sections. 88 figures. Index. viii + 236pp. 5⅜ x 8.
T440 Clothbound **$3.50**

THE FOURTH DIMENSION SIMPLY EXPLAINED, edited by H. P. Manning. 22 essays, originally Scientific American contest entries, that use a minimum of mathematics to explain aspects of 4-dimensional geometry: analogues to 3-dimensional space, 4-dimensional absurdities and curiosities (such as removing the contents of an egg without puncturing its shell), possible measurements and forms, etc. Introduction by the editor. Only book of its sort on a truly elementary level, excellent introduction to advanced works. 82 figures. 251pp. 5⅜ x 8.
T711 Paperbound **$1.35**

MATHEMATICS—INTERMEDIATE TO ADVANCED

General

INTRODUCTION TO APPLIED MATHEMATICS, Francis D. Murnaghan. A practical and thoroughly sound introduction to a number of advanced branches of higher mathematics. Among the selected topics covered in detail are: vector and matrix analysis, partial and differential equations, integral equations, calculus of variations, Laplace transform theory, the vector triple product, linear vector functions, quadratic and bilinear forms, Fourier series, spherical harmonics, Bessel functions, the Heaviside expansion formula, and many others. Extremely useful book for graduate students in physics, engineering, chemistry, and mathematics. Index. 111 study exercises with answers. 41 illustrations. ix + 389pp. 5⅜ x 8½.
S1042 Paperbound **$2.00**

OPERATIONAL METHODS IN APPLIED MATHEMATICS, H. S. Carslaw and J. C. Jaeger. Explanation of the application of the Laplace Transformation to differential equations, a simple and effective substitute for more difficult and obscure operational methods. Of great practical value to engineers and to all workers in applied mathematics. Chapters on: Ordinary Linear Differential Equations with Constant Coefficients;; Electric Circuit Theory; Dynamical Applications; The Inversion Theorem for the Laplace Transformation; Conduction of Heat; Vibrations of Continuous Mechanical Systems; Hydrodynamics; Impulsive Functions; Chains of Differential Equations; and other related matters. 3 appendices. 153 problems, many with answers. 22 figures. xvi + 359pp. 5⅜ x 8½. S1011 Paperbound **$2.25**

APPLIED MATHEMATICS FOR RADIO AND COMMUNICATIONS ENGINEERS, C. E. Smith. No extraneous material here!—only the theories, equations, and operations essential and immediately useful for radio work. Can be used as refresher, as handbook of applications and tables, or as full home-study course. Ranges from simplest arithmetic through calculus, series, and wave forms, hyperbolic trigonometry, simultaneous equations in mesh circuits, etc. Supplies applications right along with each math topic discussed. 22 useful tables of functions, formulas, logs, etc. Index. 166 exercises, 140 examples, all with answers. 95 diagrams. Bibliography. x + 336pp. 5⅜ x 8. S141 Paperbound **$1.75**

Algebra, group theory, determinants, sets, matrix theory

ALGEBRAS AND THEIR ARITHMETICS, L. E. Dickson. Provides the foundation and background necessary to any advanced undergraduate or graduate student studying abstract algebra. Begins with elementary introduction to linear transformations, matrices, field of complex numbers; proceeds to order, basal units, modulus, quaternions, etc.; develops calculus of linears sets, describes various examples of algebras including invariant, difference, nilpotent, semi-simple. "Makes the reader marvel at his genius for clear and profound analysis," Amer. Mathematical Monthly. Index. xii + 241pp. 5⅜ x 8. S616 Paperbound **$1.50**

THE THEORY OF EQUATIONS WITH AN INTRODUCTION TO THE THEORY OF BINARY ALGEBRAIC FORMS, W. S. Burnside and A. W. Panton. Extremely thorough and concrete discussion of the theory of equations, with extensive detailed treatment of many topics curtailed in later texts. Covers theory of algebraic equations, properties of polynomials, symmetric functions, derived functions, Horner's process, complex numbers and the complex variable, determinants and methods of elimination, invariant theory (nearly 100 pages), transformations, introduction to Galois theory, Abelian equations, and much more. Invaluable supplementary work for modern students and teachers. 759 examples and exercises. Index in each volume. Two volume set. Total of xxiv + 604pp. 5⅜ x 8.
S714 Vol I Paperbound **$1.85**
S715 Vol II Paperbound **$1.85**
The set **$3.70**

COMPUTATIONAL METHODS OF LINEAR ALGEBRA, V. N. Faddeeva, translated by **C. D. Benster.** First English translation of a unique and valuable work, the only work in English presenting a systematic exposition of the most important methods of linear algebra—classical and contemporary. Shows in detail how to derive numerical solutions of problems in mathematical physics which are frequently connected with those of linear algebra. Theory as well as individual practice. Part I surveys the mathematical background that is indispensable to what follows. Parts II and III, the conclusion, set forth the most important methods of solution, for both exact and iterative groups. One of the most outstanding and valuable features of this work is the 23 tables, double and triple checked for accuracy. These tables will not be found elsewhere. Author's preface. Translator's note. New bibliography and index. x + 252pp. 5⅜ x 8. S424 Paperbound **$1.95**

ALGEBRAIC EQUATIONS, E. Dehn. Careful and complete presentation of Galois' theory of algebraic equations; theories of Lagrange and Galois developed in logical rather than historical form, with a more thorough exposition than in most modern books. Many concrete applications and fully-worked-out examples. Discusses basic theory (very clear exposition of the symmetric group); isomorphic, transitive, and Abelian groups; applications of Lagrange's and Galois' theories; and much more. Newly revised by the author. Index. List of Theorems. xi + 208pp. 5⅜ x 8. S697 Paperbound **$1.45**

Differential equations, ordinary and partial; integral equations

INTRODUCTION TO THE DIFFERENTIAL EQUATIONS OF PHYSICS, L. Hopf. Especially valuable to the engineer with no math beyond elementary calculus. Emphasizing intuitive rather than formal aspects of concepts, the author covers an extensive territory. Partial contents: Law of causality, energy theorem, damped oscillations, coupling by friction, cylindrical and spherical coordinates, heat source, etc. Index. 48 figures. 160pp. 5⅜ x 8.
S120 Paperbound **$1.25**

INTRODUCTION TO THE THEORY OF LINEAR DIFFERENTIAL EQUATIONS, E. G. Poole. Authoritative discussions of important topics, with methods of solution more detailed than usual, for students with background of elementary course in differential equations. Studies existence theorems, linearly independent solutions; equations with constant coefficients; with uniform analytic coefficients; regular singularities; the hypergeometric equation; conformal representation; etc. Exercises. Index. 210pp. 5⅜ x 8. S629 Paperbound **$1.65**

DIFFERENTIAL EQUATIONS FOR ENGINEERS, P. Franklin. Outgrowth of a course given 10 years at M. I. T. Makes most useful branch of pure math accessible for practical work. Theoretical basis of D.E.'s; solution of ordinary D.E.'s and partial derivatives arising from heat flow, steady-state temperature of a plate, wave equations; analytic functions; convergence of Fourier Series. 400 problems on electricity, vibratory systems, other topics. Formerly "Differential Equations for Electrical Engineers." Index 41 illus. 307pp. 5⅜ x 8.
S601 Paperbound **$1.65**

DIFFERENTIAL EQUATIONS, F. R. Moulton. A detailed, rigorous exposition of all the non-elementary processes of solving ordinary differential equations. Several chapters devoted to the treatment of practical problems, especially those of a physical nature, which are far more advanced than problems usually given as illustrations. Includes analytic differential equations; variations of a parameter; integrals of differential equations; analytic implicit functions; problems of elliptic motion; sine-amplitude functions; deviation of formal bodies; Cauchy-Lipschitz process; linear differential equations with periodic coefficients; differential equations in infinitely many variations; much more. Historical notes. 10 figures. 222 problems. Index. xv + 395pp. 5⅜ x 8. S451 Paperbound **$2.00**

DIFFERENTIAL AND INTEGRAL EQUATIONS OF MECHANICS AND PHYSICS (DIE DIFFERENTIAL- UND INTEGRALGLEICHUNGEN DER MECHANIK UND PHYSIK), edited by P. Frank and R. von Mises. Most comprehensive and authoritative work on the mathematics of mathematical physics available today in the United States: the standard, definitive reference for teachers, physicists, engineers, and mathematicians—now published (in the original German) at a relatively inexpensive price for the first time! Every chapter in this 2,000-page set is by an expert in his field: Carathéodory, Courant, Frank, Mises, and a dozen others. Vol I, on mathematics, gives concise but complete coverages of advanced calculus, differential equations, integral equations, and potential, and partial differential equations. Index. xxiii + 916pp. Vol. II (physics): classical mechanics, optics, continuous mechanics, heat conduction and diffusion, the stationary and quasi-stationary electromagnetic field, electromagnetic oscillations, and wave mechanics. Index. xxiv + 1106pp. Two volume set. Each volume available separately. 5⅝ x 8⅜.
S787 Vol I Clothbound **$7.50**
S788 Vol II Clothbound **$7.50**
The set **$15.00**

LECTURES ON CAUCHY'S PROBLEM, J. Hadamard. Based on lectures given at Columbia, Rome, this discusses work of Riemann, Kirchhoff, Volterra, and the author's own research on the hyperbolic case in linear partial differential equations. It extends spherical and cylindrical waves to apply to all (normal) hyperbolic equations. Partial contents: Cauchy's problem, fundamental formula, equations with odd number, with even number of independent variables; method of descent. 32 figures. Index. iii + 316pp. 5⅜ x 8. S105 Paperbound **$1.75**

THEORY OF DIFFERENTIAL EQUATIONS, A. R. Forsyth. Out of print for over a decade, the complete 6 volumes (now bound as 3) of this monumental work represent the most comprehensive treatment of differential equations ever written. Historical presentation includes in 2500 pages every substantial development. Vol. 1, 2: EXACT EQUATIONS, PFAFF'S PROBLEM; ORDINARY EQUATIONS, NOT LINEAR: methods of Grassmann, Clebsch, Lie, Darboux; Cauchy's theorem; branch points; etc. Vol. 3, 4: ORDINARY EQUATIONS, NOT LINEAR; ORDINARY LINEAR EQUATIONS: Zeta Fuchsian functions, general theorems on algebraic integrals, Brun's theorem, equations with uniform periodic coffiecients, etc. Vol. 4, 5: PARTIAL DIFFERENTIAL EQUATIONS: 2 existence-theorems, equations of theoretical dynamics, Laplace transformations, general transformation of equations of the 2nd order, much more. Indexes. Total of 2766pp. 5⅜ x 8. S576-7-8 Clothbound: the set **$15.00**

PARTIAL DIFFERENTIAL EQUATIONS OF MATHEMATICAL PHYSICS, A. G. Webster. A keystone work in the library of every mature physicist, engineer, researcher. Valuable sections on elasticity, compression theory, potential theory, theory of sound, heat conduction, wave propagation, vibration theory. Contents include: deduction of differential equations, vibrations, normal functions, Fourier's series, Cauchy's method, boundary problems, method of Riemann-Volterra. Spherical, cylindrical, ellipsoidal harmonics, applications, etc. 97 figures. vii + 440pp. 5⅜ x 8. S263 Paperbound **$2.00**

ELEMENTARY CONCEPTS OF TOPOLOGY, P. Alexandroff. First English translation of the famous brief introduction to topology for the beginner or for the mathematician not undertaking extensive study. This unusually useful intuitive approach deals primarily with the concepts of complex, cycle, and homology, and is wholly consistent with current investigations. Ranges from basic concepts of set-theoretic topology to the concept of Betti groups. "Glowing example of harmony between intuition and thought," David Hilbert. Translated by A. E. Farley. Introduction by D. Hilbert. Index. 25 figures. 73pp. 5⅜ x 8. S747 Paperbound **$1.00**

Number theory

INTRODUCTION TO THE THEORY OF NUMBERS, L. E. Dickson. Thorough, comprehensive approach with adequate coverage of classical literature, an introductory volume beginners can follow. Chapters on divisibility, congruences, quadratic residues & reciprocity, Diophantine equations, etc. Full treatment of binary quadratic forms without usual restriction to integral coefficients. Covers infinitude of primes, least residues, Fermat's theorem, Euler's phi function, Legendre's symbol, Gauss's lemma, automorphs, reduced forms, recent theorems of Thue & Siegel, many more. Much material not readily available elsewhere. 239 problems. Index. I figure. viii + 183pp. 5⅜ x 8. S342 Paperbound **$1.65**

ELEMENTS OF NUMBER THEORY, I. M. Vinogradov. Detailed 1st course for persons without advanced mathematics; 95% of this book can be understood by readers who have gone no farther than high school algebra. Partial contents: divisibility theory, important number theoretical functions, congruences, primitive roots and indices, etc. Solutions to both problems and exercises. Tables of primes, indices, etc. Covers almost every essential formula in elementary number theory! Translated from Russian. 233 problems, 104 exercises. viii + 227pp. 5⅜ x 8. S259 Paperbound **$1.60**

THEORY OF NUMBERS and DIOPHANTINE ANALYSIS, R. D. Carmichael. These two complete works in one volume form one of the most lucid introductions to number theory, requiring only a firm foundation in high school mathematics. "Theory of Numbers," partial contents: Eratosthenes' sieve, Euclid's fundamental theorem, G.C.F. and L.C.M. of two or more integers, linear congruences, etc "Diophantine Analysis": rational triangles, Pythagorean triangles, equations of third, fourth, higher degrees, method of functional equations, much more. "Theory of Numbers": 76 problems. Index. 94pp. "Diophantine Analysis": 222 problems. Index. 118pp. 5⅜ x 8. S529 Paperbound **$1.35**

Numerical analysis, tables

MATHEMATICAL TABLES AND FORMULAS, Compiled by Robert D. Carmichael and Edwin R. Smith. Valuable collection for students, etc. Contains all tables necessary in college algebra and trigonometry, such as five-place common logarithms, logarithmic sines and tangents of small angles, logarithmic trigonometric functions, natural trigonometric functions, four-place antilogarithms, tables for changing from sexagesimal to circular and from circular to sexagesimal measure of angles, etc. Also many tables and formulas not ordinarily accessible, including powers, roots, and reciprocals, exponential and hyperbolic functions, ten-place logarithms of prime numbers, and formulas and theorems from analytical and elementary geometry and from calculus. Explanatory introduction. viii + 269pp. 5⅜ x 8½. S111 Paperbound **$1.00**

MATHEMATICAL TABLES, H. B. Dwight. Unique for its coverage in one volume of almost every function of importance in applied mathematics, engineering, and the physical sciences. Three extremely fine tables of the three trig functions and their inverse functions to thousandths of radians; natural and common logarithms; squares, cubes; hyperbolic functions and the inverse hyperbolic functions; $(a^2 + b^2)$ exp. ½a; complete elliptic integrals of the 1st and 2nd kind; sine and cosine integrals; exponential integrals Ei(x) and Ei(—x); binomial coefficients; factorials to 250; surface zonal harmonics and first derivatives; Bernoulli and Euler numbers and their logs to base of 10; Gamma function; normal probability integral; over 60 pages of Bessel functions; the Riemann Zeta function. Each table with formulae generally used, sources of more extensive tables, interpolation data, etc. Over half have columns of differences, to facilitate interpolation. Introduction. Index. viii + 231pp. 5⅜ x 8. S445 Paperbound **$1.75**

TABLES OF FUNCTIONS WITH FORMULAE AND CURVES, E. Jahnke & F. Emde. The world's most comprehensive 1-volume English-text collection of tables, formulae, curves of transcendent functions. 4th corrected edition, new 76-page section giving tables, formulae for elementary functions—not in other English editions. Partial contents: sine, cosine, logarithmic integral; factorial function; error integral; theta functions; elliptic integrals, functions; Legendre, Bessel, Riemann, Mathieu, hypergeometric functions, etc. Supplementary books. Bibliography. Indexed. "Out of the way functions for which we know no other source," SCIENTIFIC COMPUTING SERVICE, Ltd. 212 figures. 400pp. 5⅜ x 8. S133 Paperbound **$2.00**

CHEMISTRY AND PHYSICAL CHEMISTRY

ORGANIC CHEMISTRY, F. C. Whitmore. The entire subject of organic chemistry for the practicing chemist and the advanced student. Storehouse of facts, theories, processes found elsewhere only in specialized journals. Covers aliphatic compounds (500 pages on the properties and synthetic preparation of hydrocarbons, halides, proteins, ketones, etc.), alicyclic compounds, aromatic compounds, heterocyclic compounds, organophosphorus and organometallic compounds. Methods of synthetic preparation analyzed critically throughout. Includes much of biochemical interest. "The scope of this volume is astonishing," INDUSTRIAL AND ENGINEERING CHEMISTRY. 12,000-reference index. 2387-item bibliography. Total of x + 1005pp. 5⅜ x 8. Two volume set. S700 Vol I Paperbound **$2.25**
S701 Vol II Paperbound **$2.25**
The set **$4.50**

THE MODERN THEORY OF MOLECULAR STRUCTURE, Bernard Pullman. A reasonably popular account of recent developments in atomic and molecular theory. Contents: The Wave Function and Wave Equations (history and bases of present theories of molecular structure); The Electronic Structure of Atoms (Description and classification of atomic wave functions, etc.); Diatomic Molecules; Non-Conjugated Polyatomic Molecules; Conjugated Polyatomic Molecules; The Structure of Complexes. Minimum of mathematical background needed. New translation by David Antin of "La Structure Moleculaire." Index. Bibliography. vii + 87pp. 5⅜ x 8½. S987 Paperbound **$1.00**

CATALYSIS AND CATALYSTS, Marcel Prettre, Director, Research Institute on Catalysis. This brief book, translated into English for the first time, is the finest summary of the principal modern concepts, methods, and results of catalysis. Ideal introduction for beginning chemistry and physics students. Chapters: Basic Definitions of Catalysis (true catalysis and generalization of the concept of catalysis); The Scientific Bases of Catalysis (Catalysis and chemical thermodynamics, catalysis and chemical kinetics); Homogeneous Catalysis (acid-base catalysis, etc.); Chain Reactions; Contact Masses; Heterogeneous Catalysis (Mechanisms of contact catalyses, etc.); and Industrial Applications (acids and fertilizers, petroleum and petroleum chemistry, rubber, plastics, synthetic resins, and fibers). Translated by David Antin. Index. vi + 88pp. 5⅜ x 8½. S998 Paperbound **$1.00**

POLAR MOLECULES, Pieter Debye. This work by Nobel laureate Debye offers a complete guide to fundamental electrostatic field relations, polarizability, molecular structure. Partial contents: electric intensity, displacement and force, polarization by orientation, molar polarization and molar refraction, halogen-hydrides, polar liquids, ionic saturation, dielectric constant, etc. Special chapter considers quantum theory. Indexed. 172pp. 5⅜ x 8.
S64 Paperbound **$1.50**

THE ELECTRONIC THEORY OF ACIDS AND BASES, W. F. Luder and Saverio Zuffanti. The first full systematic presentation of the electronic theory of acids and bases—treating the theory and its ramifications in an uncomplicated manner. Chapters: Historical Background; Atomic Orbitals and Valence; The Electronic Theory of Acids and Bases; Electrophilic and Electrodotic Reagents; Acidic and Basic Radicals; Neutralization; Titrations with Indicators; Displacement; Catalysis; Acid Catalysis; Base Catalysis; Alkoxides and Catalysts; Conclusion. Required reading for all chemists. Second revised (1961) eidtion, with additional examples and references. 3 figures. 9 tables. Index. Bibliography xii + 165pp. 5⅜ x 8.
S201 Paperbound **$1.50**

KINETIC THEORY OF LIQUIDS, J. Frenkel. Regarding the kinetic theory of liquids as a generalization and extension of the theory of solid bodies, this volume covers all types of arrangements of solids, thermal displacements of atoms, interstitial atoms and ions, orientational and rotational motion of molecules, and transition between states of matter. Mathematical theory is developed close to the physical subject matter. 216 bibliographical footnotes. 55 figures. xi + 485pp. 5⅜ x 8. S95 Paperbound **$2.55**

THE PRINCIPLES OF ELECTROCHEMISTRY, D. A. MacInnes. Basic equations for almost every subfield of electrochemistry from first principles, referring at all times to the soundest and most recent theories and results; unusually useful as text or as reference. Covers coulometers and Faraday's Law, electrolytic conductance, the Debye-Hueckel method for the theoretical calculation of activity coefficients, concentration cells, standard electrode potentials, thermodynamic ionization constants, pH, potentiometric titrations, irreversible phenomena, Planck's equation, and much more. "Excellent treatise," AMERICAN CHEMICAL SOCIETY JOURNAL. "Highly recommended," CHEMICAL AND METALLURGICAL ENGINEERING. 2 Indices. Appendix. 585-item bibliography. 137 figures. 94 tables. ii + 478pp. 5⅝ x 8⅜.
S52 Paperbound **$2.45**

THE PHASE RULE AND ITS APPLICATION, Alexander Findlay. Covering chemical phenomena of 1, 2, 3, 4, and multiple component systems, this "standard work on the subject" (NATURE, London), has been completely revised and brought up to date by A. N. Campbell and N. O. Smith. Brand new material has been added on such matters as binary, tertiary liquid equilibria, solid solutions in ternary systems, quinary systems of salts and water. Completely revised to triangular coordinates in ternary systems, clarified graphic representation, solid models, etc. 9th revised edition. Author, subject indexes. 236 figures. 505 footnotes, mostly bibliographic. xii + 494pp. 5⅜ x 8. S91 Paperbound **$2.50**

PHYSICS

General physics

FOUNDATIONS OF PHYSICS, R. B. Lindsay & H. Margenau. Excellent bridge between semi-popular works & technical treatises. A discussion of methods of physical description, construction of theory; valuable for physicist with elementary calculus who is interested in ideas that give meaning to data, tools of modern physics. Contents include symbolism, mathematical equations; space & time foundations of mechanics; probability; physics & continua; electron theory; special & general relativity; quantum mechanics; causality. "Thorough and yet not overdetailed. Unreservedly recommended," NATURE (London). Unabridged, corrected edition. List of recommended readings. 35 illustrations. xi + 537pp. 5⅜ x 8.
S377 Paperbound **$2.75**

FUNDAMENTAL FORMULAS OF PHYSICS, ed. by D. H. Menzel. Highly useful, fully inexpensive reference and study text, ranging from simple to highly sophisticated operations. Mathematics integrated into text—each chapter stands as short textbook of field represented. Vol. 1: Statistics, Physical Constants, Special Theory of Relativity, Hydrodynamics, Aerodynamics, Boundary Value Problems in Math. Physics; Viscosity, Electromagnetic Theory, etc. Vol. 2: Sound, Acoustics, Geometrical Optics, Electron Optics, High-Energy Phenomena, Magnetism, Biophysics, much more. Index. Total of 800pp. 5⅜ x 8.
Vol. 1 S595 Paperbound **$2.00**
Vol. 2 S596 Paperbound **$2.00**

MATHEMATICAL PHYSICS, D. H. Menzel. Thorough one-volume treatment of the mathematical techniques vital for classic mechanics, electromagnetic theory, quantum theory, and relativity. Written by the Harvard Professor of Astrophysics for junior, senior, and graduate courses, it gives clear explanations of all those aspects of function theory, vectors, matrices, dyadics, tensors, partial differential equations, etc., necessary for the understanding of the various physical theories. Electron theory, relativity, and other topics seldom presented appear here in considerable detail. Scores of definitions, conversion factors, dimensional constants, etc. "More detailed than normal for an advanced text . . . excellent set of sections on Dyadics, Matrices, and Tensors," JOURNAL OF THE FRANKLIN INSTITUTE. Index. 193 problems, with answers. x + 412pp. 5⅜ x 8. S56 Paperbound **$2.00**

THE SCIENTIFIC PAPERS OF J. WILLARD GIBBS. All the published papers of America's outstanding theoretical scientist (except for "Statistical Mechanics" and "Vector Analysis"). Vol I (thermodynamics) contains one of the most brilliant of all 19th-century scientific papers—the 300-page "On the Equilibrium of Heterogeneous Substances," which founded the science of physical chemistry, and clearly stated a number of highly important natural laws for the first time; 8 other papers complete the first volume. Vol II includes 2 papers on dynamics, 8 on vector analysis and multiple algebra, 5 on the electromagnetic theory of light, and 6 miscellaneous papers. Biographical sketch by H. A. Bumstead. Total of xxxvi + 718pp. 5⅝ x 8⅜.
S721 Vol I Paperbound **$2.50**
S722 Vol II Paperbound **$2.00**
The set **$4.50**

BASIC THEORIES OF PHYSICS, Peter Gabriel Bergmann. Two-volume set which presents a critical examination of important topics in the major subdivisions of classical and modern physics. The first volume is concerned with classical mechanics and electrodynamics: mechanics of mass points, analytical mechanics, matter in bulk, electrostatics and magnetostatics, electromagnetic interaction, the field waves, special relativity, and waves. The second volume (Heat and Quanta) contains discussions of the kinetic hypothesis, physics and statistics, stationary ensembles, laws of thermodynamics, early quantum theories, atomic spectra, probability waves, quantization in wave mechanics, approximation methods, and abstract quantum theory. A valuable supplement to any thorough course or text.
Heat and Quanta: Index. 8 figures. x + 300pp. 5⅜ x 8½. S968 Paperbound **$1.75**
Mechanics and Electrodynamics: Index. 14 figures. vii + 280pp. 5⅜ x 8½.
S969 Paperbound **$1.75**

THEORETICAL PHYSICS, A. S. Kompaneyets. One of the very few thorough studies of the subject in this price range. Provides advanced students with a comprehensive theoretical background. Especially strong on recent experimentation and developments in quantum theory. Contents: Mechanics (Generalized Coordinates, Lagrange's Equation, Collision of Particles, etc.), Electrodynamics (Vector Analysis, Maxwell's equations, Transmission of Signals, Theory of Relativity, etc.), Quantum Mechanics (the Inadequacy of Classical Mechanics, the Wave Equation, Motion in a Central Field, Quantum Theory of Radiation, Quantum Theories of Dispersion and Scattering, etc.), and Statistical Physics (Equilibrium Distribution of Molecules in an Ideal Gas, Boltzmann statistics, Bose and Fermi Distribution, Thermodynamic Quantities, etc.). Revised to 1961. Translated by George Yankovsky, authorized by Kompaneyets. 137 exercises. 56 figures. 529pp. 5⅜ x 8½. S972 Paperbound **$2.50**

ANALYTICAL AND CANONICAL FORMALISM IN PHYSICS, André Mercier. A survey, in one volume, of the variational principles (the key principles—in mathematical form—from which the basic laws of any one branch of physics can be derived) of the several branches of physical theory, together with an examination of the relationships among them. Contents: the Lagrangian Formalism, Lagrangian Densities, Canonical Formalism, Canonical Form of Electrodynamics, Hamiltonian Densities, Transformations, and Canonical Form with Vanishing Jacobian Determinant. Numerous examples and exercises. For advanced students ...

MATHEMATICAL PUZZLES AND RECREATIONS

AMUSEMENTS IN MATHEMATICS, Henry Ernest Dudeney. The foremost British originator of mathematical puzzles is always intriguing, witty, and paradoxical in this classic, one of the largest collections of mathematical amusements. More than 430 puzzles, problems, and paradoxes. Mazes and games, problems on number manipulation, unicursal and other route problems, puzzles on measuring, weighing, packing, age, kinship, chessboards, joining, crossing river, plane figure dissection, and many others. Solutions. More than 450 illustrations. vii + 258pp. 5⅜ x 8. T473 Paperbound **$1.25**

SYMBOLIC LOGIC and THE GAME OF LOGIC, Lewis Carroll. "Symbolic Logic" is not concerned with modern symbolic logic, but is instead a collection of over 380 problems posed with charm and imagination, using the syllogism, and a fascinating diagrammatic method of drawing conclusions. In "The Game of Logic," Carroll's whimsical imagination devises a logical game played with 2 diagrams and counters (included) to manipulate hundreds of tricky syllogisms. The final section, "Hit or Miss" is a lagniappe of 101 additional puzzles in the delightful Carroll manner. Until this reprint edition, both of these books were rarities costing up to $15 each. Symbolic Logic: Index, xxxi + 199pp. The Game of Logic: 96pp. Two vols. bound as one. 5⅜ x 8. T492 Paperbound **$1.50**

MAZES AND LABYRINTHS: A BOOK OF PUZZLES, W. Shepherd. Mazes, formerly associated with mystery and ritual, are still among the most intriguing of intellectual puzzles. This is a novel and different collection of 50 amusements that embody the principle of the maze: mazes in the classical tradition; 3-dimensional, ribbon, and Möbius-strip mazes; hidden messages; spatial arrangements; etc.—almost all built on amusing story situations. 84 illustrations. Essay on maze psychology. Solutions. xv + 122pp. 5⅜ x 8. T731 Paperbound **$1.00**

MATHEMATICAL RECREATIONS, M. Kraitchik. Some 250 puzzles, problems, demonstrations of recreational mathematics for beginners & advanced mathematicians. Unusual historical problems from Greek, Medieval, Arabic, Hindu sources: modern problems based on "mathematics without numbers," geometry, topology, arithmetic, etc. Pastimes derived from figurative numbers, Mersenne numbers, Fermat numbers; fairy chess, latruncles, reversi, many topics. Full solutions. Excellent for insights into special fields of math. 181 illustrations. 330pp. 5⅜ x 8. T163 Paperbound **$1.75**

MATHEMATICAL PUZZLES OF SAM LOYD, Vol. I, selected and edited by M. Gardner. Puzzles by the greatest puzzle creator and innovator. Selected from his famous "Cyclopedia of Puzzles," they retain the unique style and historical flavor of the originals. There are posers based on arithmetic, algebra, probability, game theory, route tracing, topology, counter, sliding block, operations research, geometrical dissection. Includes his famous "14-15" puzzle which was a national craze, and his "Horse of a Different Color" which sold millions of copies. 117 of his most ingenious puzzles in all, 120 line drawings and diagrams. Solutions. Selected references. xx + 167pp. 5⅜ x 8. T498 Paperbound **$1.00**

MY BEST PUZZLES IN MATHEMATICS, Hubert Phillips ("Caliban"). Caliban is generally considered the best of the modern problemists. Here are 100 of his best and wittiest puzzles, selected by the author himself from such publications as the London Daily Telegraph, and each puzzle is guaranteed to put even the sharpest puzzle detective through his paces. Perfect for the development of clear thinking and a logical mind. Complete solutions are provided for every puzzle. x + 107pp. 5⅜ x 8½. T91 Paperbound **$1.00**

MY BEST PUZZLES IN LOGIC AND REASONING, H. Phillips ("Caliban"). 100 choice, hitherto unavailable puzzles by England's best-known problemist. No special knowledge needed to solve these logical or inferential problems, just an unclouded mind, nerves of steel, and fast reflexes. Data presented are both necessary and just sufficient to allow one unambiguous answer. More than 30 different types of puzzles, all ingenious and varied, many one of a kind, that will challenge the expert, please the beginner. Original publication. 100 puzzles, full solutions. x + 107pp. 5⅜ x 8½. T119 Paperbound **$1.00**

MATHEMATICAL PUZZLES FOR BEGINNERS AND ENTHUSIASTS, G. Mott-Smith. 188 mathematical puzzles to test mental agility. Inference, interpretation, algebra, dissection of plane figures, geometry, properties of numbers, decimation, permutations, probability, all enter these delightful problems. Puzzles like the Odic Force, How to Draw an Ellipse, Spider's Cousin, more than 180 others. Detailed solutions. Appendix with square roots, triangular numbers, primes, etc. 135 illustrations. 2nd revised edition. 248pp. 5⅜ x 8. T198 Paperbound **$1.00**

MATHEMATICS, MAGIC AND MYSTERY, Martin Gardner. Card tricks, feats of mental mathematics, stage mind-reading, other "magic" explained as applications of probability, sets, theory of numbers, topology, various branches of mathematics. Creative examination of laws and their applications with scores of new tricks and insights. 115 sections discuss tricks wtih cards, dice, coins; geometrical vanishing tricks, dozens of others. No sleight of hand needed; mathematics guarantees success. 115 illustrations. xii + 174pp. 5⅜ x 8. T335 Paperbound **$1.00**

RECREATIONS IN THE THEORY OF NUMBERS: THE QUEEN OF MATHEMATICS ENTERTAINS, Albert H. Beiler. The theory of numbers is often referred to as the "Queen of Mathematics." In this book Mr. Beiler has compiled the first English volume to deal exclusively with the recreational aspects of number theory, an inherently recreational branch of mathematics. The author's clear style makes for enjoyable reading as he deals with such topics as: perfect numbers, amicable numbers, Fermat's theorem, Wilson's theorem, interesting properties of digits, methods of factoring, primitive roots, Euler's function, polygonal and figurate numbers, Mersenne numbers, congruence, repeating decimals, etc. Countless puzzle problems, with full answers and explanations. For mathematicians and mathematically-inclined laymen, etc. New publication. 28 figures. 9 illustrations. 103 tables. Bibliography at chapter ends. vi + 247pp. 5⅜ x 8½. T1096 Paperbound **$1.85**

PAPER FOLDING FOR BEGINNERS, W. D. Murray and F. J. Rigney. A delightful introduction to the varied and entertaining Japanese art of origami (paper folding), with a full crystal-clear text that anticipates every difficulty; over 275 clearly labeled diagrams of all important stages in creation. You get results at each stage, since complex figures are logically developed from simpler ones. 43 different pieces are explained: place mats, drinking cups, bonbon boxes, sailboats, frogs, roosters, etc. 6 photographic plates. 279 diagrams. 95pp. 5⅝ x 8⅜. T713 Paperbound **$1.00**

1800 RIDDLES, ENIGMAS AND CONUNDRUMS, Darwin A. Hindman. Entertaining collection ranging from hilarious gags to outrageous puns to sheer nonsense—a welcome respite from sophisticated humor. Children, toastmasters, and practically anyone with a funny bone will find these zany riddles tickling and eminently repeatable. Sample: "Why does Santa Claus always go down the chimney?" "Because it soots him." Some old, some new—covering a wide variety of subjects. New publication. iii + 154pp. 5⅜ x 8½. T1059 Paperbound **$1.00**

EASY-TO-DO ENTERTAINMENTS AND DIVERSIONS WITH CARDS, STRING, COINS, PAPER AND MATCHES, R. M. Abraham. Over 300 entertaining games, tricks, puzzles, and pastimes for children and adults. Invaluable to anyone in charge of groups of youngsters, for party givers, etc. Contains sections on card tricks and games, making things by paperfolding—toys, decorations, and the like; tricks with coins, matches, and pieces of string; descriptions of games; toys that can be made from common household objects; mathematical recreations; word games; and 50 miscellaneous entertainments. Formerly "Winter Nights Entertainments." Introduction by Lord Baden Powell. 329 illustrations. v + 186pp. 5⅜ x 8. T921 Paperbound **$1.00**

DIVERSIONS AND PASTIMES WITH CARDS, STRING, PAPER AND MATCHES, R. M. Abraham. Another collection of amusements and diversion for game and puzzle fans of all ages. Many new paperfolding ideas and tricks, an extensive section on amusements with knots and splices, two chapters of easy and not-so-easy problems, coin and match tricks, and lots of other parlor pastimes from the agile mind of the late British problemist and gamester. Corrected and revised version. Illustrations. 160pp. 5⅜ x 8½. T1127 Paperbound **$1.00**

STRING FIGURES AND HOW TO MAKE THEM: A STUDY OF CAT'S-CRADLE IN MANY LANDS, Caroline Furness Jayne. In a simple and easy-to-follow manner, this book describes how to make 107 different string figures. Not only is looping and crossing string between the fingers a common youthful diversion, but it is an ancient form of amusement practiced in all parts of the globe, especially popular among primitive tribes. These games are fun for all ages and offer an excellent means for developing manual dexterity and coordination. Much insight also for the anthropological observer on games and diversions in many different cultures. Index. Bibliography. Introduction by A. C. Haddon, Cambridge University. 17 full-page plates. 950 illustrations. xxiii + 407pp. 5⅜ x 8½. T152 Paperbound **$2.00**

CRYPTANALYSIS, Helen F. Gaines. (Formerly ELEMENTARY CRYPTANALYSIS.) A standard elementary and intermediate text for serious students. It does not confine itself to old material, but contains much that is not generally known, except to experts. Concealment, Transposition, Substitution ciphers; Vigenere, Kasiski, Playfair, multafid, dozens of other techniques. Appendix with sequence charts, letter frequencies in English, 5 other languages, English word frequencies. Bibliography. 167 codes. New to this edition: solution to codes. vi + 230pp. 5⅜ x 8. T97 Paperbound **$2.00**

MAGIC SQUARES AND CUBES, W. S. Andrews. Only book-length treatment in English, a thorough non-technical description and analysis. Here are nasik, overlapping, pandiagonal, serrated squares; magic circles, cubes, spheres, rhombuses. Try your hand at 4-dimensional magical figures! Much unusual folklore and tradition included. High school algebra is sufficient. 754 diagrams and illustrations. viii + 419pp. 5⅜ x 8. T658 Paperbound **$1.85**

CALIBAN'S PROBLEM BOOK: MATHEMATICAL, INFERENTIAL, AND CRYPTOGRAPHIC PUZZLES, H. Phillips ("Caliban"), S. T. Shovelton, G. S. Marshall. 105 ingenious problems by the greatest living creator of puzzles based on logic and inference. Rigorous, modern, piquant, and reflecting their author's unusual personality, these intermediate and advanced puzzles all involve the ability to reason clearly through complex situations; some call for mathematical knowledge, ranging from algebra to number theory. Solutions. xi + 180pp. 5⅜ x 8. T736 Paperbound **$1.25**

FICTION

THE LAND THAT TIME FORGOT and THE MOON MAID, Edgar Rice Burroughs. In the opinion of many, Burroughs' best work. The first concerns a strange island where evolution is individual rather than phylogenetic. Speechless anthropoids develop into intelligent human beings within a single generation. The second projects the reader far into the future and describes the first voyage to the Moon (in the year 2025), the conquest of the Earth by the Moon, and years of violence and adventure as the enslaved Earthmen try to regain possession of their planet. "An imaginative tour de force that keeps the reader keyed up and expectant," NEW YORK TIMES. Complete, unabridged text of the original two novels (three parts in each). 5 illustrations by J. Allen St. John. vi + 552pp. 5⅜ x 8½.
T1020 Clothbound **$3.75**
T358 Paperbound **$2.00**

AT THE EARTH'S CORE, PELLUCIDAR, TANAR OF PELLUCIDAR: THREE SCIENCE FICTION NOVELS BY EDGAR RICE BURROUGHS. Complete, unabridged texts of the first three Pellucidar novels. Tales of derring-do by the famous master of science fiction. The locale for these three related stories is the inner surface of the hollow Earth where we discover the world of Pellucidar, complete with all types of bizarre, menacing creatures, strange peoples, and alluring maidens—guaranteed to delight all Burroughs fans and a wide circle of advenutre lovers. Illustrated by J. Allen St. John and P. F. Berdanier. vi + 433pp. 5⅜ x 8½.
T1051 Paperbound **$2.00**

THE PIRATES OF VENUS and LOST ON VENUS: TWO VENUS NOVELS BY EDGAR RICE BURROUGHS. Two related novels, complete and unabridged. Exciting adventure on the planet Venus with Earthman Carson Napier broken-field running through one dangerous episode after another. All lovers of swashbuckling science fiction will enjoy these two stories set in a world of fascinating societies, fierce beasts, 5000-ft. trees, lush vegetation, and wide seas. Illustrations by Fortunino Matania. Total of vi + 340pp. 5⅜ x 8½. T1053 Paperbound **$1.75**

A PRINCESS OF MARS and A FIGHTING MAN OF MARS: TWO MARTIAN NOVELS BY EDGAR RICE BURROUGHS. "Princess of Mars" is the very first of the great Martian novels written by Burroughs, and it is probably the best of them all; it set the pattern for all of his later fantasy novels and contains a thrilling cast of strange peoples and creatures and the formula of Olympian heroism amidst ever-fluctuating fortunes which Burroughs carries off so successfully. "Fighting Man" returns to the same scenes and cities—many years later. A mad scientist, a degenerate dictator, and an indomitable defender of the right clash—with the fate of the Red Planet at stake! Complete, unabridged reprinting of original editions. Illustrations by F. E. Schoonover and Hugh Hutton. v + 356pp. 5⅜ x 8½.
T1140 Paperbound **$1.75**

THREE MARTIAN NOVELS, Edgar Rice Burroughs. Contains: Thuvia, Maid of Mars; The Chessmen of Mars; and The Master Mind of Mars. High adventure set in an imaginative and intricate conception of the Red Planet. Mars is peopled with an intelligent, heroic human race which lives in densely populated cities and with fierce barbarians who inhabit dead sea bottoms. Other exciting creatures abound amidst an inventive framework of Martian history and geography. Complete unabridged reprintings of the first edition. 16 illustrations by J. Allen St. John. vi + 499pp. 5⅜ x 8½. T39 Paperbound **$1.85**

THREE PROPHETIC NOVELS BY H. G. WELLS, edited by E. F. Bleiler. Complete texts of "When the Sleeper Wakes" (1st book printing in 50 years), "A Story of the Days to Come," "The Time Machine" (1st complete printing in book form). Exciting adventures in the future are as enjoyable today as 50 years ago when first printed. Predict TV, movies, intercontinental airplanes, prefabricated houses, air-conditioned cities, etc. First important author to foresee problems of mind control, technological dictatorships. "Absolute best of imaginative fiction," N. Y. Times. Introduction. 335pp. 5⅜ x 8. T605 Paperbound **$1.50**

28 SCIENCE FICTION STORIES OF H. G. WELLS. Two full unabridged novels, MEN LIKE GODS and STAR BEGOTTEN, plus 26 short stories by the master science-fiction writer of all time. Stories of space, time, invention, exploration, future adventure—an indispensable part of the library of everyone interested in science and adventure. PARTIAL CONTENTS: Men Like Gods, The Country of the Blind, In the Abyss, The Crystal Egg, The Man Who Could Work Miracles, A Story of the Days to Come, The Valley of Spiders, and 21 more! 928pp. 5⅜ x 8.
T265 Clothbound **$4.50**

THE WAR IN THE AIR, IN THE DAYS OF THE COMET, THE FOOD OF THE GODS: THREE SCIENCE FICTION NOVELS BY H. G. WELLS. Three exciting Wells offerings bearing on vital social and philosophical issues of his and our own day. Here are tales of air power, strategic bombing, East vs. West, the potential miracles of science, the potential disasters from outer space, the relationship between scientific advancement and moral progress, etc. First reprinting of "War in the Air" in almost 50 years. An excellent sampling of Wells at his storytelling best. Complete, unabridged reprintings. 16 illustrations. 645pp. 5⅜ x 8½.
T1135 Paperbound **$2.00**

SEVEN SCIENCE FICTION NOVELS, H. G. Wells. Full unabridged texts of 7 science-fiction novels of the master. Ranging from biology, physics, chemistry, astronomy to sociology and other studies, Mr. Wells extrapolates whole worlds of strange and intriguing character. "One will have to go far to match this for entertainment, excitement, and sheer pleasure . . . ," NEW YORK TIMES. Contents: The Time Machine, The Island of Dr. Moreau, First Men in the Moon, The Invisible Man, The War of the Worlds, The Food of the Gods, In the Days of the Comet. 1015pp. 5⅜ x 8. T264 Clothbound **$4.50**

BEST GHOST STORIES OF J. S. LE FANU, Selected and introduced by E. F. Bleiler. LeFanu is deemed the greatest name in Victorian supernatural fiction. Here are 16 of his best horror stories, including 2 nouvelles: "Carmilla," a classic vampire tale couched in a perverse eroticism, and "The Haunted Baronet." Also: "Sir Toby's Will," "Green Tea," "Schalken the Painter," "Ultor de Lacy," "The Familiar," etc. The first American publication of about half of this material: a long-overdue opportunity to get a choice sampling of LeFanu's work. New selection (1964). 8 illustrations. 5⅜ x 8⅜. T415 Paperbound **$1.85**

THE WONDERFUL WIZARD OF OZ, L. F. Baum. Only edition in print with all the original W. W. Denslow illustrations in full color—as much a part of "The Wizard" as Tenniel's drawings are for "Alice in Wonderland." "The Wizard" is still America's best-loved fairy tale, in which, as the author expresses it, "The wonderment and joy are retained and the heartaches and nightmares left out." Now today's young readers can enjoy every word and wonderful picture of the original book. New introduction by Martin Gardner. A Baum bibliography. 23 full-page color plates. viii + 268pp. 5⅜ x 8. T691 Paperbound **$1.50**

GHOST AND HORROR STORIES OF AMBROSE BIERCE, Selected and introduced by E. F. Bleiler. 24 morbid, eerie tales—the cream of Bierce's fiction output. Contains such memorable pieces as "The Moonlit Road," "The Damned Thing," "An Inhabitant of Carcosa," "The Eyes of the Panther," "The Famous Gilson Bequest," "The Middle Toe of the Right Foot," and other chilling stories, plus the essay, "Visions of the Night" in which Bierce gives us a kind of rationale for his aesthetic of horror. New collection (1964). xxii + 199pp. 5⅜ x 8⅜. T767 Paperbound **$1.00**

HUMOR

MR. DOOLEY ON IVRYTHING AND IVRYBODY, Finley Peter Dunne. Since the time of his appearance in 1893, "Mr. Dooley," the fictitious Chicago bartender, has been recognized as America's most humorous social and political commentator. Collected in this volume are 102 of the best Dooley pieces—all written around the turn of the century, the height of his popularity. Mr. Dooley's Irish brogue is employed wittily and penetratingly on subjects which are just as fresh and relevant today as they were then: corruption and hypocrisy of politicans, war preparations and chauvinism, automation, Latin American affairs, superbombs, etc. Other articles range from Rudyard Kipling to football. Selected with an introduction by Robert Hutchinson. xii + 244pp. 5⅜ x 8½. T626 Paperbound **$1.00**

RUTHLESS RHYMES FOR HEARTLESS HOMES and MORE RUTHLESS RHYMES FOR HEARTLESS HOMES, Harry Graham ("Col. D. Streamer"). A collection of Little Willy and 48 other poetic "disasters." Graham's funniest and most disrespectful verse, accompanied by original illustrations. Nonsensical, wry humor which employs stern parents, careless nurses, uninhibited children, practical jokers, single-minded golfers, Scottish lairds, etc. in the leading roles. A precursor of the "sick joke" school of today. This volume contains, bound together for the first time, two of the most perennially popular books of humor in England and America. Index. vi + 69pp. 5⅜ x 8. T930 Paperbound **75¢**

A WHIMSEY ANTHOLOGY, Collected by Carolyn Wells. 250 of the most amusing rhymes ever written. Acrostics, anagrams, palindromes, alphabetical jingles, tongue twisters, echo verses, alliterative verses, riddles, mnemonic rhymes, interior rhymes, over 40 limericks, etc. by Lewis Carroll, Edward Lear, Joseph Addison, W. S. Gilbert, Christina Rossetti, Chas. Lamb, James Boswell, Hood, Dickens, Swinburne, Leigh Hunt, Harry Graham, Poe, Eugene Field, and many others. xiv + 221pp. 5⅜ x 8½. T195 Paperbound **$1.25**

MY PIOUS FRIENDS AND DRUNKEN COMPANIONS and MORE PIOUS FRIENDS AND DRUNKEN COMPANIONS, Songs and ballads of Conviviality Collected by Frank Shay. Magnificently illuminated by John Held, Jr. 132 ballads, blues, vaudeville numbers, drinking songs, cowboy songs, sea chanties, comedy songs, etc. of the Naughty Nineties and early 20th century. Over a third are reprinted with music. Many perennial favorites such as: The Band Played On, Frankie and Johnnie, The Old Grey Mare, The Face on the Bar-room Floor, etc. Many others unlocatable elsewhere: The Dog-Catcher's Child, The Cannibal Maiden, Don't Go in the Lion's Cage Tonight, Mother, etc. Complete verses and introductions to songs. Unabridged republication of first editions, 2 Indexes (song titles and first lines and choruses). Introduction by Frank Shay. 2 volumes bounds as 1. Total of xvi + 235pp. 5⅜ x 8½. T946 Paperbound **$1.25**

MAX AND MORITZ, Wilhelm Busch. Edited and annotated by H. Arthur Klein. Translated by H. Arthur Klein, M. C. Klein, and others. The mischievous high jinks of Max and Moritz, Peter and Paul, Ker and Plunk, etc. are delightfully captured in sketch and rhyme. (Companion volume to "Hypocritical Helena.") In addition to the title piece, it contians: Ker and Plunk; Two Dogs and Two Boys; The Egghead and the Two Cut-ups of Corinth; Deceitful Henry; The Boys and the Pipe; Cat and Mouse; and others. (Original German text with accompanying English translations.) Afterword by H. A. Klein. vi + 216pp. 5⅜ x 8½.
T181 Paperbound **$1.15**

THROUGH THE ALIMENTARY CANAL WITH GUN AND CAMERA: A FASCINATING TRIP TO THE INTERIOR, Personally Conducted by George S. Chappell. In mock-travelogue style, the amusing account of an imaginative journey down the alimentary canal. The "explorers" enter the esophagus, round the Adam's Apple, narrowly escape from a fierce Amoeba, struggle through the impenetrable Nerve Forests of the Lumbar Region, etc. Illustrated by the famous cartoonist, Otto Soglow, the book is as much a brilliant satire of academic pomposity and professional travel literature as it is a clever use of the facts of physiology for supremely comic purposes. Preface by Robert Benchley. Author's Foreword. 1 Photograph. 17 illustrations by O. Soglow. xii + 114pp. 5⅜ x 8½. T376 Paperbound **$1.00**

THE BAD CHILD'S BOOK OF BEASTS, MORE BEASTS FOR WORSE CHILDREN, and A MORAL ALPHABET, H. Belloc. Hardly an anthology of humorous verse has appeared in the last 50 years without at least a couple of these famous nonsense verses. But one must see the entire volumes—with all the delightful original illustrations by Sir Basil Blackwood—to appreciate fully Belloc's charming and witty verses that play so subacidly on the platitudes of life and morals that beset his day—and ours. A great humor classic. Three books in one. Total of 157pp. 5⅜ x 8. T749 Paperbound **$1.00**

THE DEVIL'S DICTIONARY, Ambrose Bierce. Sardonic and irreverent barbs puncturing the pomposities and absurdities of American politics, business, religion, literature, and arts, by the country's greatest satirist in the classic tradition. Epigrammatic as Shaw, piercing as Swift, American as Mark Twain, Will Rogers, and Fred Allen. Bierce will always remain the favorite of a small coterie of enthusiasts, and of writers and speakers whom he supplies with "some of the most gorgeous witticisms of the English language." (H. L. Mencken) Over 1000 entries in alphabetical order. 144pp. 5⅜ x 8. T487 Paperbound **$1.00**

THE COMPLETE NONSENSE OF EDWARD LEAR. This is the only complete edition of this master of gentle madness available at a popular price. A BOOK OF NONSENSE, NONSENSE SONGS, MORE NONSENSE SONGS AND STORIES in their entirety with all the old favorites that have delighted children and adults for years. The Dong With A Luminous Nose, The Jumblies, The Owl and the Pussycat, and hundreds of other bits of wonderful nonsense. 214 limericks, 3 sets of Nonsense Botany, 5 Nonsense Alphabets. 546 drawings by Lear himself, and much more. 320pp. 5⅜ x 8. T167 Paperbound **$1.00**

SINGULAR TRAVELS, CAMPAIGNS, AND ADVENTURES OF BARON MUNCHAUSEN, R. E. Raspe, with 90 illustrations by Gustave Doré. The first edition in over 150 years to reestablish the deeds of the Prince of Liars exactly as Raspe first recorded them in 1785—the genuine Baron Munchausen, one of the most popular personalities in English literature. Included also are the best of the many sequels, written by other hands. Introduction on Raspe by J. Carswell. Bibliography of early editions. xliv + 192pp. 5⅜ x 8. T698 Paperbound **$1.00**

HOW TO TELL THE BIRDS FROM THE FLOWERS, R. W. Wood. How not to confuse a carrot with a parrot, a grape with an ape, a puffin with nuffin. Delightful drawings, clever puns, absurd little poems point out farfetched resemblances in nature. The author was a leading physicist. Introduction by Margaret Wood White. 106 illus. 60pp. 5⅜ x 8.
T523 Paperbound **75¢**

JOE MILLER'S JESTS OR, THE WITS VADE-MECUM. The original Joe Miller jest book. Gives a keen and pungent impression of life in 18th-century England. Many are somewhat on the bawdy side and they are still capable of provoking amusement and good fun. This volume is a facsimile of the original "Joe Miller" first published in 1739. It remains the most popular and influential humor book of all time. New introduction by Robert Hutchinson. xxi + 70pp. 5⅜ x 8½. T423 Paperbound **$1.00**

Prices subject to change without notice.

Dover publishes books on art, music, philosophy, literature, languages, history, social sciences, psychology, handcrafts, orientalia, puzzles and entertainments, chess, pets and gardens, books explaining science, intermediate and higher mathematics, mathematical physics, engineering, biological sciences, earth sciences, classics of science, etc. Write to:

Dept. catrr.
Dover Publications, Inc.
180 Varick Street, N.Y. 14, N.Y.